Spherophylon

The Integrated Lives of Earth's Diverse Organisms

Spherophylon

THE INTEGRATED LIVES OF EARTH'S
DIVERSE ORGANISMS

KUNIO IWATSUKI

BOOKEND PUBLISHING CO., LTD.

Spherophylon
The Integrated Lives of Earth's Diverse Organisms

Published in 2023 by Bookend Publishing Co., Ltd., Tokyo.
The cash portion of an International Cosmos Prize awarded to the
author defrayed part of the production expenses for this book, and
the Expo '90 Foundation has provided distribution assistance.

Book Design by Lapisworks

Printing and binding by Nissha Printing Communications, Inc.

ISBN978-4-907083-81-6 C0040

FOREWORD

Peter H. Raven
President Emeritus
Missouri Botanical Garden, St. Louis, Missouri

Over the course of his distinguished career in the realm of systematic botany, Professor Kunio Iwatsuki has found time to reflect seriously on the nature of life. His views, summarized in this book, open important new visions for its readers, presenting ideas and concepts that will inspire thought about the meaning of the challenges that we face together. Professor Iwatsuki's thinking incorporates elements of traditional Japanese views of these areas, which makes his book all the more useful and interesting for those of us concerned with life on Earth and its future.

The past five centuries have seen the emergence of global commerce, which, while opening many new vistas for us, has tended to homogenize our thinking. During this period, the global human population has increased dramatically from about 500 million people to nearly eight billion, with the prospect of increasing by another two or three billion before reaching stability. We have enabled our growth with successive applications of new technologies, and by doing so we have made ourselves increasingly distinct from other living things. Regardless of how we view nature, we now have the obligation to determine not only our future but that of all of the other organisms on Earth. As Professor Iwatsuki helps us realize, it is no longer adequate to speak in terms of "the preservation of nature," but rather it has become necessary to define terms for the harmonious coexistence of human beings *with* nature.

Based on his reflections on these matters, Professor Iwatsuki has developed the concept of the "spherophylon." This concept is most usefully understood in relation to the meaning of two other widely used terms, "biological diversity" and "biodiversity." Thomas Lovejoy coined the first of these in 1980 to reflect the species diversity existing at an individual locality or more widely. Our increasing awareness of massive biological extinction led to the organization of a symposium at the US National Academy of Sciences on the topic in 1985. The proceedings of that symposium, which was chaired by E. O. Wilson, first used the term biodiversity (as "BioDiversity"). Subsequently, the term "biodiversity" has been adopted widely, expanding its meaning to include all life on Earth, its genetic diversity, and its ecological relationships.

Seeking a more precise expression for all of nature, Professor Iwatsuki in 1998 introduced the term spherophylon, which he intended not only to express all of life as it currently exists, but the whole sweep of life from its origins nearly four billion years ago to the present. As you will learn from this book, Professor Iwatsuki is less concerned about extinction than are many other authors in his discussion of this term and its ramifications. His thoughts, rather, focus on the historical scope of life and the way we should view it. In doing so, he provides many interesting and novel reflections that certainly deserve our careful consideration. As one example of his thinking, the deceased contribute indirectly to the knowledge and enjoyment that we retain as living individuals as long as we remember what they thought and accomplished during the course of their lives.

This book goes on to explore the meaning of our lives in contrast to the lives of other organisms. It sets our species apart from them, discussing in that context the ongoing coexistence of people with the rest of nature. Professor Iwatsuki points out that we can prosper only through harmonious coexistence with other living things. Should these conditions be natural or artificial? We have imposed many changes on nature as our Stone Age ancestors knew it, and for a successful and sustainable future have tried to find ways to make these endure in the context of the whole. Regardless of how distinct we may consider human beings to be among all other organisms, we can truly understand ourselves only in a collective context that includes all life on Earth.

In Professor Iwatsuki's view, the development of agriculture was a wise step that enabled human beings to continue to live sustainably on this planet. In terms of his conclusion, we note that the population of human beings approximately 11,000 years ago when our ancestors first practiced agriculture consisted of only about one million people, of which only about 100,000 were living in Europe. Today we number nearly eight billion individuals, calculated to increase by nearly two billion additional people over the next 30 years; that is, the middle of the current century. Professor Iwatsuki considers this an example of our success, but I would note that others contradict this view. For example, the Global Footprint Network (www.footprintnetwork.org), using UN statistics, calculates that we are currently consuming about 175 percent of what the world can produce sustainably. In addition, we are so sharply divided into rich and poor that it is difficult to imagine a way for us to live collectively within our means. We are challenged in seeking ways to overcome these difficulties.

We live in a world that is home to many millions of other species, with some two million of them having been given scientific names. Even for the ones that we have named, we know little about the great majority, with plants and vertebrates being obvious exceptions; other groups, such as fungi, nematodes, and bacteria, are extremely poorly known. Based on what I personally regard as a misplaced hope for our developing a general definition of species, Professor Iwatsuki reviews some of our efforts to understand the world's species. The diversification of life on Earth for more than four billion years has led to the evolution of a bewildering variety of organisms with an increasingly complex web of interactions knitting them together both in space and over time. Certainly, understanding the way biodiversity is manifest both within and between species is only a part of understanding the characteristics of the spherophylon through time, a point thus far given inadequate attention. In this connection, it is important to point out that millions of individual organisms and their genes are in principle available for human use, even though we have appropriated only a small fraction of them so far.

Individual cells reproduce in various ways, some forming simple colonies and others becoming true multicellular organisms like us. Reproduction is the key characteristic of life. When individual cells form colonies, the cells may remain relatively independent, or, as in the case of animals and plants, they may become integrated within multicellular individuals. These multicellular individuals may in turn be cloned to produce other individuals identical to their progenitor. Such cloning has important practical and philosophical implications, which Professor Iwatsuki examines in the third chapter of this book. When it becomes possible to clone individual humans routinely, we will have to decide questions such as the implications of cloned human beings for our culture generally. One of the ways in which we are distinct from other organisms is the extent to which we have lengthened our individual lives beyond our original lifespans. If cloning alters the nature of our global population, the world will become a very different place from what it is now. In view of these considerations, Professor Iwatsuki wonders how we might regulate the cloning of humans, as for example if we decide to clone large numbers of people to perform some particular function. Up to this point in our history, we have mainly had to consider the vertical flow of human life through generations, but we shall soon need to deal with what we might term its *horizontal replacement* as well.

Unfortunately, as James Watson and others have pointed out, human beings seem inevitably to do whatever is possible, despite regulations to the contrary or fears we may hold initially. This generality has serious ramifications for all of our activities, and makes it especially important to consider, as carefully as we possibly can, not only the implications of human cloning, but also the ultimate impacts of many factors that already affect our lives, such as imprisonment, sexuality, and even nuclear war. Such questions inevitably bring to mind Professor Iwatsuki's reflections on whether the spherophylon in its current development has arrived at a kind of maturity like an individual animal. In his fourth chapter, he usefully discusses the limits of knowledge and the meaning of hypotheses in contemporary life, pausing briefly to deplore our current dependency on the media, whatever the quality of the information that they may offer us.

Even in defined areas such as food, we depend on very large numbers of other organisms within the spherophylon. When it comes to the maintenance of the air we breathe and the soil on which we rely, we depend on thousands, even millions, of them. We live among countless other organisms that interact with one another and with us on a continuing basis. Where we go in the future, and how rapidly the organisms on which we depend will become extinct, depends on a wisdom that we may have yet to develop. We know with certainty that global warming, driven by manmade changes in the atmosphere, will drive the extinction of many organisms over the coming decades. How extensive that extinction may be, and what its effect is likely to be on the lives of human beings, remains to be seen. It will depend, in large part, on what we actually do about the problems that we face. Like all steps that have the potential to contribute to human survival, what we actually do about them will depend on our ability to overcome innate greed and develop beneficial actions for the common good.

Because we humans depend on the health of the global ecosystem for our survival, we must do what we can to preserve it. Fortunately, the study of biodiversity has gradually assumed a greater importance over the years. We have formed a number of broadly based organizations for the study of biodiversity that are functioning now. Each of these has the potential to contribute a great deal to our common knowledge, certainly making what we learn more generally available than it would be otherwise. In any event, it seems certain that our human activities will have destroyed much of the existing spherophylon long before we know very much about it. As our knowledge expands, however, our possibilities for survival and flourishing should increase proportionately, so we must do our very best to devote sufficient energy to these studies while as many organisms as possible are still in existence.

Despite these difficulties, Professor Iwatsuki counsels us to be of good faith in investigating biodiversity and all of the conditions of our lives, despite the magnitude of the implied task. In general, however, it would seem that the estimated extinction of a third to half of all currently existing kinds of organisms during the next century will place severe limits on what we can learn in time to maintain some sort of equilibrium on our troubled planet. There are certainly strong reasons for plotting accurately what is possible for us to discover or save during the relatively few decades in which a reasonably complete spherophylon remains available to investigate.

Our future will be determined by the way we deal with other organisms, which are rapidly decreasing both in number and stability because of our relentless growth. In this context, Professor Iwatsuki wrestles with the question of our meaning and purpose, and of our proper place in the whole of life. It is estimated that less than 3 percent of the total number of species that ever existed on Earth still exist today: clearly, there have been many substantial changes in the spherophylon over the millennia. The process of change has been powerful and continuous. For that reason alone, when we try to preserve nature as it exists now, we confront a reality very different from that of our ancestors. The hominoid evolutionary branch first diverged from other African apes some six to eight million years ago; our species evolved perhaps 300,000 years ago; and we developed agriculture about 11,000 years ago. There is no way in which we can preserve all of the nature that exists now, much less that which existed at the start of our blitzkrieg of agricultural growth into all the suitable habitats on Earth. Indeed, we *must* not only develop the knowledge necessary to preserve the stability of the spherophylon as it is today, but also the wisdom to conduct our actions so that the preservation we achieve will extend into the future.

Along with many other experts, Professor Iwatsuki calls attention to the need to curb human population growth if we are to have any hope of achieving the harmonious and sustainable development of the environment. Many of us have concluded that with present knowledge we can envision the development of a sustainable Earth only with a substantial reduction in the existing human population, perhaps to no more than a quarter of its current eight billion people. The global situation today leaves many of us malnourished or hungry even as our numbers continue to expand explosively. Our individual and collective greed has led to a major separation between the wealthy and the poor. For example, the British charity Oxfam has estimated that just eight individuals control as much wealth as more than four billion of the world's relatively poor people. The strength of our selfishness makes effective action very difficult at a time when we need it the most. Indeed, relatively few of us have any latitude in the way we deal with the environment, however pure and enlightened our inspiration may be.

Many of us would question Professor Iwatsuki's notion that by inventing agriculture, our Neolithic ancestors were enhancing world stability. The fact that we are now using some 40 percent of the Earth's land surface for crops or grazing certainly limits the sustainability of the globe as a whole. The huge global disparity between rich and poor certainly limits our common ability to act in any sustainable way, given human greed and preoccupation with day-to-day life.

A final question of fundamental importance concerns the degree to which human beings, *Homo sapiens*, are distinct from other organisms. Our ability to learn and to communicate are clearly better developed than those of any other organism, but it is in our ability to accumulate information over the years and over generations that our distinctiveness is best defined. How these abilities define us as different from other species is the major subject of Professor Iwatsuki's useful chapter 5, in which echoes of both religion and philosophy are present. We have clearly modified the planet to fit our own species, setting up many of its systems to fulfill our real and perceived needs. We cannot return to some idealized situation that existed in the past, and can now succeed only by dealing with what we have left to create the best and most sustainable future for those who follow us – and perhaps for all life on Earth. Iwatsuki's thoughtful consideration of our global plight certainly helps to illuminate the difficult path that lies before us. In continuing to pursue this path, readers of this book will find it both interesting and useful.

Author's Preface

Spherophylon is a word describing the integration of the lives of all organisms on Earth; that is, life at a higher level than that of the individual. To explain the word specifically, it is necessary to consider what life is in detail. While elucidating the meaning of life is the fundamental objective of basic biology, this subject is also the target of study in philosophy, religion, medical sciences, agriculture and other academic fields, both in the natural sciences and the humanities. In this book, I, as a biologist, discuss this particular topic from a fundamental biological point of view, with special reference to the area of biodiversity research.

In the 1970s, I started an integrated research project in botany in collaboration with a group of systematic botanists and plant ecologists in Japan (Hara, 1985), though the validity of this kind of study was not fully recognized at that time by scientists in general. At the time, research on biodiversity was in such a state in general scientific society that the phrase "biological diversity" was not widely recognized, even when the Convention on Biological Diversity was a topic for discussion by the United Nations Conference on Environment and Development (the so-called Earth Summit) in 1992.

Various attempts were made to communicate the significance of biological diversity, though not much research was available. Under these circumstances, I took up the concept of biodiversity and tried to explain it to the general public from a fundamental understanding of biology. Based on my research, I proposed a new term, spherophylon, which combines the word "sphere" (from biosphere) and -phylon (from phylogeny).

This word coined in English, spherophylon, was first introduced at a symposium organized by the Royal Swedish Academy of Science in September, 1998, when I read a short paper entitled "Plant Systematics for the Twenty-First Century." The paper was printed in the proceedings of the symposium in late 1999 (Iwatsuki, 1999b). The word "spherophylon" first appeared in the book in Japanese *Seimeikei—seibutsu tayosei no atarashii kangae* (Seimeikei: a new concept of biodiversity), published by Iwanami Shoten in February, 1999 (Iwatsuki, 1999a). The concept of the spherophylon was fully described in this book, though it was in Japanese. A short summary of the concept was published in 2006 in the *Proceedings of the Japan Academy* as a review article (Iwatsuki, 2006). As no full discussion in English has been available to date, a full description of the concept of the spherophylon will be given here.

In coining this word, I hoped to expand the understanding of biodiversity among the general public, especially for the sake of environmental conservation, as the destruction of nature is proceeding rapidly: deterioration of biodiversity stands as a typical indicator of environmental destruction. At that time, I was involved in both governmental and non-governmental committees for nature conservation. The neglect of biodiversity, even by conservationists, bothered me, and I fought to bring broader attention to it. The publication of the above-mentioned papers reflected a part of my activities at that time.

Awareness of the importance of biodiversity has increased since then, though the destruction of nature remains a serious problem, as evidenced by the increasingly frequent incidence of severe nature disasters. These can be attributed to climate change caused by recent human activity. The importance of biodiversity in relation to environmental crisis cannot be overemphasized.

For this reason, I would like to return to the concept of biodiversity in terms of basic biology to discuss its significance in an environmental context.

This book addresses a broad range of information, though most concepts are covered generally, without a detailed discussion of each special topic. Readers should conduct additional research to gain the most current information in various fields. Human knowledge at the moment in any of the subjects concerned is not infallible, and some facts introduced here may be determined to be incorrect in the future. Still, I will proceed to integrate a variety of facts as known at present, arriving at the conclusion that the life of the spherophylon should be evaluated. Humans generally respect their own benefit as multicellular individuals, and we now understand that they themselves can expect to benefit from maintaining the vitality of the spherophylon.

The first step in writing this book was the translation of my Japanese book *Seimeikei* into English. Ms. Takako Iwaki translated the entirety of the original Japanese text into English. However, this book was issued nearly a quarter of a century ago, and the available information has been greatly enriched in many respects. To update the points of discussion, I rearranged the contents of this book and made some additions and reconstructions to the text. In most parts, I retained Ms. Iwaki's translation, though all the editorial responsibility is my own.

This book is composed of roughly two parts: the first half, covering chapters 1 to 4, explains the concept of the spherophylon; and the latter, chapters 5 to 7, discusses the environmental issues related to the vitality of the spherophylon. These topics are inseparable from each other, and in this book they are discussed side by side. Because these two parts are inseparably intermingled with each other, it is necessary to contain the discussions taken up here in a single book.

It is expected that this book will be read by the general public, especially young people like university undergraduates. This is not a work of biological science in a strict sense, but I would expect specialists to also be interested in this topic, and hope they will assist in drawing attention to the value of this product of biology to human culture.

The topics discussed in this book are concerned neither with religion nor the arts, though I understand that life is one of the chief issues that human culture, including these disciplines, attempts to investigate. The only reason I can't manage to include information from these disciplines in the concept of spherophylon is my short acquaintance with them; the discussion here is mostly based on biological science, even though I myself depend much on religion and arts in my daily life. I hope to have a chance to expand the discussion of the spherophylon to include these aspects, though I do not know when that will be possible.

Kunio Iwatsuki
Yokohama
November 2022

Contents

Color plates follow page 172.

Prologue: Life on Earth Now

The Living Spherophylon

Environmental degradation has been a serious issue for a long time. Unfortunately, however, we cannot say we have applied the best solution to this issue. Why is this?

We should look into why, here. On close examination, we realize that something is missing in our daily thinking and code of conduct; we fail to take an overall view of established facts, though each fact may be well known to us.

Taken individually, the facts discussed in this book are nothing new. Yet this book offers something new in that it tries to gain an overall view of the matter by looking at it from various angles. To solve issues that emerge only when they are viewed in their totality requires the integration of a seemingly ordinary individual understanding.

As can be seen a few pages in, this book discusses matters that are common knowledge. This means that each subject is discussed in simple terms. Quite often, the tone is not strictly scientific, because this book is more about helping people understand the issues than pursuing exact technical correctness. I did not want the discussion to become unnecessarily abstruse, even at the risk of its sounding unscientific.

You may not have heard of the term "spherophylon," which appears in this book's title. This is only natural, since this term, which refers to a living entity above cells and individual life-forms, is one I created myself. I coined the word by joining "phylon"—referring to life's expansion in time—and "biosphere"—referring to life's expansion in space—to signify life that exists beyond time and space, which is the very theme of this book. The purpose of this book is to discuss the life that is lived by all organisms on Earth at once, which transcends time and space, as opposed to the individual lives of cells and life-forms. This is the current reality and the future of biodiversity, particularly on Earth.

It may be worthwhile to allude here to the concept of "Gaia" proposed by Lovelock (1988). The Gaia hypothesis (originally named after a Greek goddess) recognizes the entirety of Earth as a living system; all the living organisms plus the inorganic substances that form the Earth are considered a living entity; we should love everything on Earth, as we are part of the whole living entity.

I chose to use spherophylon, as it encompasses life that may exist on other astronomical objects, not just on the planet Earth. The Gaia hypothesis considers organisms on this planet, as well as their inorganic surroundings, to form a complete unit of life; in contrast, the life-carrying body will be strictly differentiated from inorganic objects in the spherophylon concept that is discussed in this book.

I do hope that exploring the meaning of life on Earth from this perspective will offer an opportunity to readers, especially those of younger generations, to cherish even a single life as part of the spherophylon—the system maintained by the entirety of creatures existing on this planet.

The lives of humans
We usually discuss life and death as issues relating to individual human beings, mostly from the viewpoints of medical science and religion. Since the dawn of human culture, life and death have been the most important topics discussed. The main goal of medical science is to enable all human beings to have a healthy life expectancy. And religious leaders have long discussed how to overcome the fear of death. After millennia of discussions, however, we humans are still suffering from aging and declining health, as well as fear of death. Knowing little about our own life and death, we seek to understand the facts that relate to them.

The way human beings view life and death is mostly based on our culture, or our sophisticated logic. We know how to enjoy our lives, and we are afraid to face death, or the end of life. There are two aspects that make us fear death: one is that we will finish life and go to an unknown world (paradise or hell); the other is that we will suffer from possible severe pain, serious illness, and loss of dignity at the end of life. In contrast, nonhuman organisms lack the high-level culture and self-consciousness to consider life and death. In general, organisms' fear of death is based solely on their instinct; they do not develop the awareness to allow them to enjoy their lives or to fear their death. (This is, of course, the way of thinking in our culture; in truth, we do not actually know how they feel.) Nonhuman organisms do not recognize the end of their life, or death, but as organisms they react to danger in order to avoid accidental death. There are many instances in which elderly individuals of a particular species have been

Fig. 1 The history of life on Earth

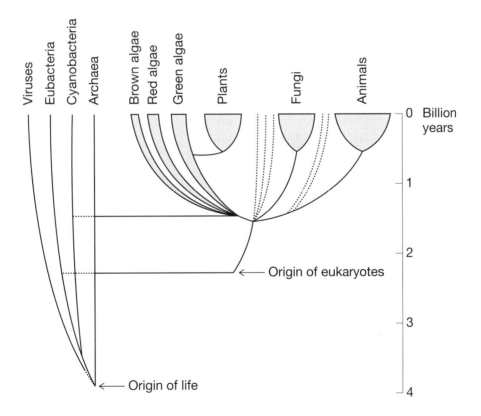

observed leaving their population when they feel their death is near. Still, this phenomenon is not comparable to religious events in human culture. Even plants, which have no brain, work to avoid death and develop their lives as widely as possible. This is the principle of life and the very foundation of evolution.

The main objective of biology is to elucidate what life is. Modern natural sciences, including biology, analyze the actual evidence in nature under the concept of materialism; that is, based on the interrelationships between the subjects. When evidence is unavailable, the relationships between the subjects are not accepted as proven facts. At this moment, we have no fully evidenced explanation on the question of what life and death are in the field of biology, or in the natural sciences in general.

Medical science, one of the applied fields of biology, seeks to maintain human health based on scientific evidence. Biology has uncovered numerous demonstrable facts, and medical science has succeeded in applying these facts to improve the ways of maintaining human health. However, medical science cannot offer any conclusive answer to the questions what life and death are. It is still not certain whether the death of brain means the death of the body itself (this is discussed in chapters 1 through 3). On this last point, medical scientists and scholars of religion have had endless debates without coming to a single conclusion.

Biology seeks to investigate the life shared by all organisms on Earth, and to define life and death for all those organisms. No conclusion with firm evidence has been arrived at in this area of research, either, and further study is sorely needed. However, we should consider a different phase of life based on the existence of biodiversity. This is where the concept of the spherophylon comes in.

It is difficult to narrowly define a living entity. When we talk about life, we usually consider the living entity to be an individual. According to modern biological knowledge, however, no individual organism can live completely on its own; an individual must collaborate with other organisms to maintain its life. It is therefore evident that any individual organism cannot live without interacting with other organisms. This being the case, what type of life are we usually discussing? Biology knows that an individual life can be duplicated by a cell, or the genetic information preserved in the DNA maintained in the nucleus of each cell. It is also a fact that a cell cannot live on its own.

In single-celled organisms, an individual cell has its own life. In multicellular organisms, all the cells that make up the individual being collaborate together to maintain the life of that being. In this way, single-celled and multicellular beings live their lives, though the pattern of life is not necessarily the same.

The question asked here is what it means for an organism to live, not why or how it is living. The organism may be an individual human being, such as you yourself; also it may also be a cell, or one of the components of a body, as well as the spherophylon of which you are a part. It is rather difficult to understand the concept of the spherophylon here, and I intend to explain in this book why I refer to the spherophylon to answer this question.

We live because we are human

What do people live for? Such a naïve question, as if asked in a bygone time by a tormented youth with a literary bent. These days, however, we need to explore the question to find an answer that suits the modern era, and this question, as in the old days, cannot have a fixed answer that applies to everyone.

The question here, however, is not a profound philosophical one. Put simply, it asks us what our goals are in life. People live in myriad ways. The reason why I live my life loving science and nature is, quite simply, because I was born as a human being. It must be the same for you. The reason why you do certain things is because you were born a human being. "Because it's there" (the famous response by the climber George Mallory, given in a 1923 interview with the *New York Times* when he was asked why he would climb a mountain in the face of a variety of unpredictable dangers) seems rather equivocating, but this is actually the best answer.

We live as people because we were born human. We are prepared to do so, since we have to live as people anyway.

This book explores the meaning of life by comparing the life of humans with that of living things in general; or rather, biodiversity with human life. You may find this juxtaposition incongruous at first. Biodiversity may be discussed as something that creates an environment for people to live in, or as something that is at odds with humans as an ecological factor and with respect to gene resources. Even so, we should not ignore the fact that all this is premised on the idea that it is a human biological trait to seek a way of life that helps humanity to prosper.

In discussions of environmental conservation or animal rights, some may say that we should protect them even if people must be sacrificed to do so. Even such extreme opinions, however, are consciously or unconsciously based on the assumption that humans will not go extinct. I have yet to meet anyone so radical that they assert that nature and animals should be saved even if it means extinguishing the human race. Protecting the environment and the organisms within it depends on the idea that people and other living organisms can coexist.

This book, then, does not intend to discuss biodiversity for its own sake; rather, it will examine the idea that biodiversity can, and should, coexist with people. That is to say, we will explore what we should do to facilitate the prosperity of humankind, discussing people and biodiversity in doing so, and going back to the question of what people live for. This eventually will lead to the conclusion that we should aim for harmonious coexistence with all other living creatures—biodiversity, in other words—for the purpose of securing success for humanity, and that we will need to endure certain inconveniences, ultimately for our own sake. This does not mean, however, that we will follow an argument that only guides us toward a predetermined conclusion; rather, we will arrive at this conclusion if we pursue the argument logically. The only reason why I offer the conclusion first here is because I want to make it clear that working toward our success by reconciling with biodiversity does engage particularly with the question of how we live.

Let us take a fresh look at the term "protecting nature" here. What are we protecting nature from? The opposite of nature is artificiality. Does this mean that we protect the environment from artificiality, or human acts? Would reducing artificiality to zero enable us to achieve ideal environmental conservation?

Historically, people, who are born of nature, have repeatedly imposed artificial changes upon nature until it is no longer in its primeval state. (It may be useful to comment on this wording. In Japan, we often use the word *shizen*—usually considered equivalent to the word "nature" in English—to refer to green areas such as *satoyama*. A *satoyama*, however, is a man-made area (see below) that could be considered a form of "secondary nature." The word "nature" should not be applied to any artificially transformed site, and strictly speaking, a *satoyama* is not a natural site, although many natural elements and wild organisms may inhabit it. Returning the environment to its original state would take artificial acts of conservation. Human activities have overtaken the planet to the extent that we are no longer able to maintain the existing environment without human intervention. It is not possible to cancel out the accumulation of human acts at this point. People, evolving within nature as one of the species that constitute nature, incessantly perform artificial acts. We cannot simply return the existing environment to the state it was in before human intervention wrought innumerable changes upon it. It might be possible to generate an environment that would be much closer to Earth's original natural state, but that would require the wholesale destruction of nature as it exists now.

Is ignorance a crime?

We discuss biodiversity, and evolution in the history of life, yet we know so little about what it means to live even now. We have merely a superficial understanding of the mechanism or the phenomenon of life, without any in-depth knowledge. This is not due to lack of intention to study; it is only on this point that science has managed to illuminate so little. We have sinned so flagrantly because we do not understand what it means to live. This ignorance is a grave crime if it causes us to inflict various wrongful acts on people, the planet, and nature. Ignorance in itself can be called a crime, and if it brings us to commit further crimes, we need to grow out of it to avoid such acts. (Crimes committed knowingly while pretending ignorance are far worse: mortal crimes.)

Because our science is still nascent, there is only so much that we can claim to know about nature. Even so, we attempt various daring acts in our relation to the environment. Such adventurous endeavors are not carried out with a solid prospect of success. They may trigger the end of the human race. Should we still persist in these wild attempts? Successful ventures require actual planning. It is a mere reckless stampede, not a daring adventure, if we forge ahead blindly into the utterly unknown without any view to success.

The premise of this book is that people should follow a path toward a glorious future. To what extent can we do that? How should we live now for that to happen? If there is any guidance on this, that is what this book will try to explore.

Learning from our Neolithic ancestors

We will seek guidance by turning to the past for precedent. The population of *Homo sapiens* was rising steadily at the end of the Paleolithic Age. Humans lived as hunter-gatherers, as resources were in ample and stable supply. If they had continued to try to support the growing population with this method of resource procurement, however, they would have caused such an impact on nature that the natural regeneration of forests would have been prevented.

Our wise ancestors, however, devised the art of breeding livestock and cultivating plants. They could have sought out more efficient ways of hunting and gathering. On that bountiful planet, it was not impossible to acquire sufficient resources to sustain the entire population, despite its growth in size—for the time being, if not for eternity. How did they know to make the right decision regarding their role in history? It was not based on any scientific rationale. As we review the history, our ancestors, who started the Neolithic Age (the New Stone Age), managed to invent a successful approach, going down the right path in history. They did sacrifice nature to human acts of destruction to some extent, but their actions did not strike a decisive blow to the entire environment on the planet. As a result, they kept a splendid practice of using biodiversity on Earth sustainably.

Our Neolithic ancestors' choice did not just enrich the particular age they lived in. Over the next 25 centuries, humanity made a beeline for prosperity, helped by the pastoral and agricultural lifestyles that had become the norm in the New Stone Age. Their choice not only brought stability to their epoch, but built a foundation for the subsequent constructive development of the human race. I paid homage to the wisdom of our Neolithic ancestors in one of my books (Iwatsuki, 1997).

Living organisms have created increasingly adaptive forms throughout the three billion years of evolutionary history. Humans—just one of the myriad diverse species—built progressively higher civilizations throughout their history. Learning about the history of life and of the human race gives us a sense of gratitude for the choices that our ancestors made. At the same time, it also gives us a sharp reminder that we now bear a similar responsibility for the future of humanity. Our Neolithic ancestors put humans on the path to the prosperous lives we lead today, in spite of the fact that they lacked a historical context to do so. In comparison, modern people can learn from the history begun by our wise ancestors.

Can we make the right choice again?
We are currently facing a grave situation akin to the one that our prehistoric ancestors faced. The global population is growing at an exponential rate. It was 5 billion in the middle of the twentieth century, but exceeded 7.5 billion recently and is presumed to reach 10 billion in the middle of this century. We have made such great progress with transportation that outer space is now within our reach, and there are discussions of people emigrating even beyond the global scale. We have seen technological revolutions that made tremendous advances in the quantity and quality of available resources, as well as techniques to tap into them. This means

that we are exhausting the planet's resources at a markedly faster rate. It will not take long before we use up all the natural resources on Earth, if we remain dependent on them. According to ecological footprint calculations by the Worldwide Fund for Nature, the current activities of modern human beings would require two Earths to be sustainable.

It may not be impossible to somehow procure sufficient resources even within a few decades or years, just as it might not have been impossible for prehistoric people to secure necessary resources by continuing their hunting and gathering ways at the end of the Paleolithic Age. Yet, if we do not change our lifestyle, we will inflict irrevocable harm on the planet's natural resources. By that point, it will be too late to panic. Modern people have the advanced science and knowledge to make an accurate, informed judgment of the reality we face, with clear understanding of the situation—and we must do so. If we continue making bad decisions and claiming ignorance, we might drive our descendants to the brink of extinction.

What decisions should we make, then? We need to acquire insight for living today—not just for the present, but with a view to being part of a long history. Our prehistoric ancestors chose successful strategies based on their instincts, not on scientific reasoning; we must discover and implement our strategies on the basis of scientific rationale and reasoning. For this purpose, we need to have a clear understanding of how our life transcends time and space. We need to seek a path that leads to the future success of humankind, from learning how life-forms have evolved. We can accomplish this by examining the life of the spherophylon on Earth.

Modern people do not seem to understand the obligations and roles of their lives very clearly. This may be because they are weighed down by daily life, too busy thinking about how to spend the day to the best of their interests. Living this way can hardly be called living life to the fullest. Let us study what it means for a person to live, and for a species to live, by analyzing the lives of various species on the planet.

Exploring biodiversity will allow us to envision our future path; the era we start must be one that aims at harmonious coexistence between nature and mankind. To illustrate this, this book will consider the meaning of our individual existence in the history of evolution of organisms, affirm the significance of our individual existence on the planet, and pursue the meaning of living a life that transcends time and space. Debating how far current biology can cope with such a life based on facts, or on inference where the facts cannot be verified, this book will explore the meaning of life for the spherophylon of planet Earth.

Spherophylon and the traditional Japanese spirit

Due to the influence of globalization, most modern Japanese people are more or less Westernized in their way of thinking, and can hardly recognize the ancient soul of their country. Many non-Japanese people, on the contrary, have a keen interest in the traditional Japanese spirit. However, it can be rather difficult for non-Japanese people to understand, especially because of linguistic barriers. This difficulty is evident in some particular terms related to traditional Japanese spirit, such as *kyousei*, *satoyama*, and *mottainai*, which are difficult to translate into Western languages (including English).

I will try to explain the concepts expressed in these terms very briefly, though it in truth each one of these complicated concepts would require its own book to explain correctly and completely. Though they are different from each other, these three terms all relate to the traditional Japanese spirit. They are usually discussed individually, but they correlate to each other at a deep conceptual level.

Kyousei

When the International Garden and Greenery Exposition was held in Osaka in 1990, the main theme of the event was summarized in a symbolic phrase: the pursuit of the "harmonious coexistence between nature and mankind." This expression, "harmonious co-existence," is the English equivalent of *kyousei*. (Incidentally, we talk about coexistence between people and nature, but not about the coexistence between chimpanzees and nature. There is, perhaps, sort of irony inherent in the expression.) In

Japanese, the word used to express "coexistence" is *kyouzon*, which has a different nuance than *kyousei*. The addition of the adjective "harmonious" for kyousei expresses this.

This guiding principle of *kyousei* between humans and nature, however, tends to fall prey to wordplay. The Japanese word *kyousei* is used to convey two different concepts. One is a biological term describing a special phenomenon wherein two species live together under an inseparable relationship. This term has been used as a Japanese translation of "symbiosis" since that word was introduced into Japanese a little more than a century ago). For example, a certain fungus and a certain alga can live together to form a kind of lichen, or a couple of male and female *Spongicola venusta* De Hahn might form a symbiotic relationship with a Venus' Flower Basket. (A derivative term, "endosymbiosis," refers to certain types of cells entering others, becoming the ancestors of mitochondrion and chloroplast in the process of eukaryote evolution.)

In some cases, however, where two species have formed a notably mutually dependent relationship such that each cannot survive without the other species, and both species were formed as a result of coevolution – as in the case of figs and fig waps – their relationship is not called symbiotic. In that sense, this Japanese word *kyousei* (*kyou* means "together," and *sei* means "life"), is used often in the more general sense of "living together," rather than as a biological term for symbiosis. This broader sense of *kyousei*, which originally came from a Buddhist concept, has been in use for several centuries. Though they had no knowledge of natural science, our ancestors in Japan lived with nature on the Japanese archipelago and had a religion rooted in nature. As a result, their way of living was well in accordance with modern biological concepts, especially with respect to their utilization of land with regional allocations, as described below.

Satoyama
When the COP 10 Convention on Biodiversity was organized in 2010 in Nagoya, Japan, the SATOYAMA Initiative was one of the proposals from

the Japanese government. The regions of the Japanese archipelago were divided into three categories: *okuyama*, *satoyama*, and *satochi* (*hitozato*).

The Japanese archipelago has a complicated structure, with a great deal of mountainous area and not many plains suitable for agriculture. To manage this, our ancestors utilized the slope of mountains for agriculture, digging out terraced fields to create a beautiful landscape. The *satochi* is the residential area where these terraced paddy fields were traditionally created. These vibrant green spaces are often characterized as areas of "secondary nature."

The *okuyama* (literally "deep mountain") areas were kept natural with fewer artificial influences. *Okuyama* were worshipped as the site of the deities: ancient Japanese people believed that their souls would go there after they passed away.

Satoyama (literally "village mountain") is the transitional zone between *okuyama* and *satochi*. People relied on these areas for natural resources, including firewood and charcoal, that could not be obtained from the limited agricultural spaces of the *satochi*. *Satoyama*, formed by humans since the Neolithic Age, functioned as a buffer zone to keep the *okuyama* natural. (In the 1960s, when UNESCO initiated the Biosphere Reserves, the core zone was recommended to be separated from transitional areas by a completely continuous buffer zone. Ancient Japanese, completely uninformed by modern biology, cultivated *satoyama* as a buffer zone.) It is a pity that *satoyama* was once translated as "countryside" by a native English person, and this is adopted in some pamphlets issued from the Agency of Environment (at that time). The countryside in Japan must be *satochi-satoyama*, a completely green area with a lot of natural elements, though *satoyama* is, in strict sense, *satoyama*-forest covered by secondary broad-leafed trees (color plate).

Mottainai

Recently, this term has been widely applied in the sense that "it is *mottainai* to throw out materials that are still useful." This has been a useful concept for expressing the need to conserve resources and not be wasteful. When the Kenyan Nobel Prize laureate Wangari M. Maathai (1940–2011) visited Japan, she was very much interested in this term and concept, and wished to disseminate them widely. In fact, this definition makes sense in the modern context, and in recent times Japanese people have easily taken to interpreting *mottainai* in this way.

However, the original concept of this term is different from this modern usage, as most dictionary definitions show. It was originally coined to express the ancient Japanese people's reverence for nature. *Mottai* is a word referring to material reality; the ancient Japanese believed a deity coexisted in everything, and thus all things were worthy of reverence. Everything around us should be carefully treated with deep respect and never disregarded, even if it is no longer useful (economically or otherwise). Under this concept, our ancestors cherished everything around them, and had an ethos of not wasting natural resources. This concept is different from the modern one in which people prioritize economic growth, evaluating only the effective use of materials. In recent times, materials are carelessly abandoned if they are considered economically valueless and therefore useless. This results in an enormous amount of waste and a huge loss of natural resources.

Why spherophylon now?

How does the concept of spherophylon benefit today's world? Recently, every contribution in any scientific field is evaluated based on its potential benefit to society, as any research always requires a tremendous budget. In the past, the set reply to this question was that the contribution was in a field of basic science, and no immediate benefit could be expected. Now, such an answer is deemed unacceptable, and an explanation of how it might be useful to society is demanded.

On the concept of the spherophylon, I have to say that it does not offer any immediate economic benefit to society, and then I have to explain why I am interested in this topic. In response to this question, I have two comments.

The first one is the timing of the contribution this will make to society. Recently, only immediate benefits to society are considered in taking decisions. However, discussions surrounding the lives of organisms—and of humans in particular—will continue endlessly, to be concluded only when science can explain everything in nature and in human knowledge. Because we do not know when we will know everything, questions about life remain open-ended, and we can only discuss the topic without coming to a conclusion. Discussion of life is something like a sophistic game, and such a discussion offers the pleasure of games. But the pleasure of new discoveries far exceeds that of playing a game with a predetermined conclusion.

Furthermore, investigations into the nature of life offer many side benefits. The biological knowledge analyzed in the course of seeking the principle of life is effectively utilized in medical sciences, and our medical treatments serve to improve the health of human beings, as well as that of our pets and livestock. It can further benefit by informing human activity. We develop nature to benefit our lives, and destruction of nature is a severe problem we are facing at present. Scientific information can help us determine the proper direction to develop, though the effects of such decisions may not be evident for at least ten years, or a century, or a millennium.

My second comment, when considering the discussion of the nature of life, is to ask what it means to benefit. These days, benefit is usually assessed based on its economic effect. The question is always, "How much does it cost?" Investigating the nature of life does not have any immediate economic benefit, and it costs nothing.

We usually consider our lives in individual terms. But how do you answer if you are asked, "How old is your life?" Most people would respond by saying their generation, or the years since their birth. This is the age stated on a government-issued identification card, or the age that society recognizes. The question, however, is "How old is your life?" not "How old are you?" All living organisms have inherited their life from their parents, as their parents did from their grandparents. No individual organism has the power to create itself independently—life can exist only when it is birthed. Thus, we know that our lives have an age of nearly four billion years, or the period since life on Earth was created.

On the other hand, no individual organism can live alone. The life of every individual organism depends in various ways on the other individual organisms, and all organisms on Earth have a direct or indirect relationship to one another.

My work in systematic botany mainly involves research on a particular taxonomic group of plants, pteridophytes. In the course of analyzing the biodiversity of species within this plant group, in addition to a wide-ranging review of species biodiversity research for the sake of university education, as well as for social education, I came to see how the concept of spherophylon relates to understanding the principle of life.

It is hard to name a specialist in the field of the life of organisms, as this subject has various aspects. In current scientific classification, there is no particular field dealing with the question of what life is; this subject is quite complicated in nature as well as in human culture. In a sense, everyone attempting to analyze life is an amateur. And generally speaking, amateurs are not considered to be authoritative in any particular field of research. Any specialized research area is quite complicated, and is concerned with a great deal of information, and an amateur does not have access to all of the information that has been amassed on that area. In such circumstances, it is rather difficult for amateurs to contribute properly. When it comes to the question of what it means to be alive, there are no professionals; anyone can contribute in their own way. This is why I am discussing the concept of spherophylon in relation to this question.

Specialists in a particular field usually report on the results they have obtained in that field, though sometimes the report is restricted strictly to information in the specific field in question. Accurate information in the field under consideration is valuable to society, but synthesis of information from various fields is also urgently needed at the moment. Topics such as the nature of life should be discussed while integrating information from a variety of relevant fields. I propose to discuss the topic of spherophylon in this way.

"To be, or not to be? That is the question." This is a famous quote by Hamlet in the classic play by William Shakespeare (1564–1616). In the following discussion, I, as a biologist, will expound on the spherophylon, expecting that this will fit into an analysis of the question of what life is.

CHAPTER
1

✳

LIFE SUPPORTED BY TIME—HOW OLD IS YOUR LIFE?

1. The Age of Life

How long have you lived?

When we talk about our life, we usually think about our own age as an individual, trying to understand life in terms of lifespan. I often put this question to audiences at universities and various other public places when I give lectures: "Here's a biological question: How many years have you been living in this world?" They'll usually give me their age as it appears on official records, or the amount of time since they were born. They might say they were 20 years old. Then I ask them, "What does that mean, biologically?" They seem to get the idea for the first time, and answer, "I was formed within my mother's womb a little earlier than that." If their twentieth birthday is on that day, I'll suggest, "Then the answer is 20 years and some nine months." They'll say yes, looking relieved. And, in fact, if my question had been, "How many years have passed since you, as an individual organism, were formed?" their answer—20 years and nine months—would be correct (we will overlook the matter of whether or not they were in the womb for exactly nine months).

Then I ask again, slightly changing the question, "Since when have you been living?" They look puzzled for a second. I paraphrase it: "Since when has your life been living?" They might not quite get the point. I explain further what I mean by this question, and say, "Seeing that you are alive, you must have life." They usually nod. I go on, "So, your life. Was it newly created when you began as an individual?" and they look like they're getting it.

At around this point, I'll ask them if they know Pasteur's swan-neck flask experiment. Some may know it, while others won't. If the latter, I explain about it briefly. Let us take a quick look at that experiment here. Not a few people believed in the spontaneous generation of life in the latter half of the nineteenth century. As the theory went, putrefactive organisms would spontaneously emerge in a boiled and sterilized meat broth, causing it to rot if left alone undisturbed. Those who opposed this theory insisted that microbes entered somehow, though they were invisible, causing the broth to putrefy; they would not emerge if the boiled broth was kept in a sealed container so that putrefactive microbes could not enter. Those in favor would argue against this, saying that the germs could not live in a sealed container.

To put an end to this discussion, Louis Pasteur (1822–1895) put meat broth in a long-necked flask with an S-shaped neck, boiled it to sterilize it, and left it for some time. The shape of the neck of the flask (called a "swan-neck flask") did not prevent air from entering. Even after a number of days, the broth did not putrefy.

This experiment demonstrated that life does not arise spontaneously in inanimate matter; life can only come from life. Since the swan-neck experiment in 1860, it has become scientific common knowledge that life does not generate itself spontaneously. In fact, before Pasteur, in 1858 Rudolf Virchow propounded the theory that all cells come from cells. Virchow's hypothesis was based on the cell theory, a theory that all organisms are composed of the basic units of cells, which had been proposed by Mattias Schleiden for plants in 1838 and Theodor Schwann for animals in 1839.

Over three billion years of life
Life can only exist where life already exists, as a successor of a life that came before. Explained this much, the earlier question—how long has the life that you now possess been alive—comes into a sharper focus. My audience is able to accept the explanation more easily that they are alive

because they received life from their parents, rather than that a new life was created when they, as individuals, started. Then, their parents also received life from their parents, they from theirs, and so it goes. At this point, my audience truly understands the question. They can follow me when I tell them that if they went back in time some millions of years, they would see their life was in a more monkey-like life-form, and then it was living in a fish-like life-form some hundreds of million years ago, and that eventually they would see it was in a bacteria-like life-form three billion years ago.

We could actually trace back the history of our life to the very beginning of life on Earth, which is estimated to have occurred some four billion years ago. Some students tell me candidly that they could only relate to life going back to their grandparents' generation. In response, I ask them to consider objective facts, rather than whether they can relate to them or not. Then, they can understand that life contained in our individual bodies has been alive for over three billion years without interruption, since life was generated on Earth.

One individual may be born when that particular life-form is generated; yet our life has been living for more than three billion years, passing through various life-forms that constitute individual organisms.

What we need to further consider here is that it is not only human life that has been living all this time. Every animate organism around us also has lived the same three-billion-plus years. Every living thing on Earth has lived over three billion years. The grains of rice you had for breakfast this morning, the grains of wheat that the bread was made of, the cotton that turned into the clothes you are wearing now, the trees that provided the lumber to make your desk and chair, the coliform bacteria living inside your body, and the cockroach that you swatted this morning—all living things carry life that has continued to live all through the three-billion-plus years without any interruption.

Incidentally, it is not at all rude to ask ladies the age of the life they contain for this very reason. The correct answer is, "Every living thing is equally over three billion years old." You, I, and everyone have a life that is over three billion years old.

2. The Age of the Materials that Form Individual Organisms

How old is your body?
Organisms are composed of a variety of materials. This person that is you is an aggregate of an astronomical number of atoms. Without a body that is made of physical matter, there is no being that you can call your own self.

If you said earlier that your age as an individual was 20 years and nine months old, it means that you have owned your individual life-form for that duration of time. Now let us examine the physical matter that constitutes a life-form.

How many of the physical substances that compose your body are your own? The elements that constitute living organisms are predominantly

Table 1 Weight ratios of most-prevalent elements in human body

Element	Atomic symbol	Weight ratio (%) in human body	Weight ratio (%) in Earth's surface
Oxygen	O	65.0	46.6
Carbon	C	18.5	0.03
Hydrogen	H	9.5	0.14
Nitrogen	N	3.3	trace
Calcium	Ca	1.5	3.6
Phosphorus	P	1.0	0.07
Potassium	K	0.4	2.6
Sulfur	S	0.3	0.03
Chlorine	Cl	0.2	0.01
Sodium	Na	0.2	2.8
Magnesium	Mg	0.1	2.1
Silicon	Si	trace	27.7

Sources: Various

hydrogen (H), oxygen (O), carbon (C), and nitrogen (N). These elements make up the water, carbohydrates, fat, protein, nucleic acids, and other molecules that form the individual body.

Since when have you possessed this colossal number of atoms that are the building blocks of the body that you regard as your individual self? When I put this question to people who have accepted the fact that their life is over three billion years old, they look oddly guarded, wary of another trick question, and ask in return, "Since I was born, or since I was conceived?"

The atoms that make up your body, at least those that are involved in forming living tissues, do not stay put once they become part of the body. These atoms are constantly interchanged with other atoms of the same elements. For example, molecules consist of elements such as oxygen and carbon. While the proportions of the elements do not change, the individual atoms—oxygen and carbon in this example—are continually replaced by other atoms of the same elements. This is called dynamic equilibrium.

What is the speed at which the atoms that form living organisms repeat the process of becoming combined with and then separated from particular molecules? On average, in a three-month period, one third of the atoms become detached from molecules and are replaced by others. At this speed, it is assumed that most of the atoms that constitute the body are replaced by other atoms of the same elements in one year.

And now, I put this question to you: "How long has your body been yours?" Your atoms, the basic substance that makes up your body, have been in your possession only for about one year at the most. You may have thought that you have lived as an individual for some 20 years, but the individual atoms that your body is composed of are not yours for more than one year; your atoms are—thus your body is—not even one year old. (Remember, I am talking here about the atoms composing your living body. You have some attached materials which are not alive themselves; hair and nails are easily understandable examples, and you can keep your hair for more than one year if you do not cut or remove it.)

I would add here a discussion of the sustainability of the cells that make up your body. As noted above, your basic life-form is not your multicellular body, but the cells comprising your body. The human body is composed of some 37 trillion cells. These cells comprising your body are not permanently yours throughout your lifespan. According to cytologists' research, more than 90 percent of cells are swapped with the other cells of the same nature; thus, your body is a constantly transforming aggregate of different cells produced by division. Every day, you shed the dead cells as dirt, or cut your hair or nails, or excrete them in various ways.

The body is young forever

What does this mean? Say, you meet up with a friend that you have not seen for a whole year. You shake hands with the friend, saying, "I haven't seen you in ages! How are you?" This person that you say you have not seen for some time is a container of life, a life-form that is composed of completely different atoms from one year ago. If you place more significance on matter, you should actually say, as if to a stranger, "It's nice to meet you." Your friend, whom you have not seen for a year, is actually a life-form that is an aggregate of completely different atoms than before.

What is it that you have not seen for a year, then? Even in a case like this, most people do not think of individual atoms when talking about matter. We do not relate to individual atoms at all; matter, for us, means our skin and flesh. Our thinking goes like this: even if atoms are gradually replaced day by day, this skin and this flesh are mine, and so the body I had a year ago is the same as the body I have now; they are both me.

Let us examine this on something more tangible. Hair and nails are dead tissues, and they do not show life activities that signify dynamic equilibrium. Yet even structures like hair and nails that are not alive in themselves grow daily with the activities of living tissues, demonstrating clearly that they are part of a living organism. Hair is the clearest example of how your body today is a nearly completely different one from last year, as you have it cut regularly. People understand this when I ask them if the hair and nails that they have now have been the same since they were born.

All living organisms are life-forms consisting of an aggregation of substances. There is no life that does not have a body. The atoms that constitute a life-form do not remain in an individual for more than one year. This is not only true of human beings: Every living creature is continually replacing basic units of substances, day in and day out, as long as they are engaged in life activities. This is exactly what it means to live.

Then how old is the basic unit of substances that form your life? In answer to this question, you would not insist on 20-some years. They are one year old at the most. You, along with the living organisms that make up the food you eat, the materials for your clothes and house, your colon bacilli, cockroaches, and any other living creature, do not live in life-forms that are made of the same substances even for one year.

So I tell my audiences, "You have only had that wonderful body of yours for a year at most. How young you are! You should have no fear you will age at all. You will always have a fresh body that is less than one year old. Enjoy your youth."

3. The Age of an Individual

When are individuals born?

When we talk about human life, we always have our own in mind. Even when we think about someone else's life, we cannot help comparing it with our own.

As demonstrated above, our life has been alive for over three billion years. This life is always contained in a life-form—our bodies, in the case of humans—and this life-form is composed of substances.

Those who are celebrating their twentieth birthday today may say they are 20 years old; yet that is only a social construct. They have been living as individuals for 20 years and nine months. Biologically, this figure is easier to understand and more significant.

The term of 20 years is the duration of time since they started living as a separate entity after leaving their mother's womb. We hardly talk about embryos or fetuses having the dignity of individuals while their life is completely dependent on the mother for the first nine months. Yet, are we so self-reliant since the moment we are born? Is there any fundamental difference between a fetus, whose every need is met inside the womb, and a newborn baby who is living under its parents' protection once it leaves the womb? Just like kangaroo babies, which grow up in their mother's pouch, human infants have no possibility of survival without parental protection. Maybe the only significant difference is that they are now able to survive as long as they are cared for by anyone, whereas their mother is their only caretaker while they are still in the womb.

Here, it is not appropriate to allude to the social aspect of the life of a fetus; countries define it by their own laws. The treatment of a dead fetus, either by abortion or miscarriage, is different depending on the country and the length of time the fetus has remained in the womb. This will be discussed later.

Your official age is only a product of a social agreement on how ages are counted. People made that agreement, which means it can be remade with their consent; yet when we become accustomed to social conventions, we become so entrenched in them that we get into the habit of even comprehending the meaning of something like life that must have an objective existence based on that fiction. Then, we even perceive the meaning of life—what it means to live—in the framework of that social convention.

This is not to say that this way of counting age should be denounced. As a social convention, it is so entrenched that we are hardly aware of it. Life, however, has other various aspects; we should not forget that we always find a different meaning in it, looking at it from a different perspective.

In this case, let us summarize the birth of an individual. Usually, a newborn baby is recognizable in multicellular organisms. In observing the life cycle of any species, the starting point of a new generation is considered to occur at the time of reproduction. Organisms having the alternation of generation perform reproduction in two ways: zygosis of two gametes, including fertilization of egg cell and sperm in sexual species, and the formation of spores after reduction division. (The details of the biological process of reproduction will not be described here.)

In the case of unicellular organisms, the starting point of new individuals, or a new generation, occurs with every cell division. In this type of reproduction, a new generation starts without leaving any corpse or dead cells; it is simply the same phenomenon that is performed in the normal cell division of every multicellular organism.

Death: the end of a lifespan

As components of the spherophylon, the lives of organisms continue endlessly, or every organism carries its life that has survived for more than 30 billion years. In this sense, life does not have a natural end, aside from accidental death. Still, we often talk about death, and it is a serious matter for every human culture.

When we consider life in the common sense, we usually think about death at the end of our lifespan. What is this death that concerns us, then?

Our image of death comes from seeing a dead body. This type of death is typical of multicellular organisms. Here, we would consider death in its basic biological sense.

If we consider the minimum level of life, the life of a cell stands as a basic unit. In fact, the origin of life was certainly accomplished when a cell first appeared. Organic substances are just substances, not living matter, but we can see a living organism when the structure of a cell is established. A cell carries out life functions and self-reproduction. However, we should realize that all the materials comprising a cell are passed on to its daughter cells when the cell reproduces. When a cell divides into two daughter cells, nothing remains after the mother cell "dies," passing its life on to the daughter cells. In unicellular organisms, cell division is equivalent to the normal reproduction of multicellular organisms, or the formation of a new generation that succeeds its parents.

Unicellular organisms carry on their generations simply through cell division, and no dead body is left behind in the process of a new individual being born. The mother cells escape aging by cell division, which produces a new generation. Outside of accidental death introduced by environmental conditions, the death of a cell does not produce a corpse.

The evolution of multicellular organisms created diversification in the morphology and function of cells. A variety of cells, however, carry out cell division just as unicellular organisms do. As elements of a multicellular body, cells regulate their metabolism and escape from aging. In contrast with unicellular organisms, however, multicellular organisms evolved a new method of reproduction, in which a particular reproductive cell is differentiated, and this particular type of cell is what carries out generational change.

There are multicellular bodies that are not involved in reproduction. Such a body lives without any concern for reproduction, and ages over time. The multicellular body grows older, and its components (various organs and tissues) begin to wear out. Finally, the multicellular body becomes unable to continue its living activity, and completes (finishes) its life, leaving a corpse which is not alive, and is not a living thing. Usually, the length of multicellular body's life is fixed as its particular life-span, depending on the species. This is the evolution of natural death (It is not necessary here to allude to accidental death).

Organisms show their awareness of death in their physiological reactions, though no organisms except for humankind considers death to be the cessation of brain activity (sophistic reaction). For human beings, the death of an individual brings cultural problems, though that is not a topic to be discussed here. In studying the death of human beings more deeply in our culture, we should also look to philosophy and religion.

Summarizing the above discussion, I would comment here that the life of an organism is carried on by its offspring, if there are any, ensuring that it is alive even after death. I would comment further that, in the case of modern human society, dead people usually have an active influence on those in their culture who are still living, as noted below.

Medical treatments and human brain death

As noted above, unicellular organisms (either primitive or extant) living in a single cell reproduce by cell division; the two daughter cells consist of materials inherited from their mother cell. This means that unicellular organisms have no natural death (by aging) to remain corpse. Multicellular organisms, on the contrary, produce the next generation of offspring by a special reproductive process, and the parents live even after their offspring inherit their genes. After a certain amount of time, however, the bodies of aged individuals naturally end their life through the phenomenon called death, leaving behind their dead bodies. For humans, death became a topic to be dealt with.

What does it mean for a person to die, then? Is brain death the death of an individual human being? What does it mean for an individual to have had its time?

The death of a human is not the same as the death of another individual organism. This is because human death is no longer the natural death of a living thing; it has become entangled with artificial technology; that is, medical practice.

There was no room to question the use of cardiac arrest in determination of death until recently. Progress in medical technology has made it possible, however, to keep the heart functioning even in a state of brain death. Therefore, it is possible for a human body to maintain the functions of its owner's life even when the brain becomes inactive. Then it becomes quite problematic to determine at which point to declare the death of the individual. This is not only a medical issue, but is related to the fundamental meaning of living (though maybe we should discuss the life of people, who are conscious of living, and that of organisms living in nature separately).

Apparently, it is not possible to bring someone who is in a state of brain death back to normal life by artificially pumping blood through the heart. The definition of "normal life" here is having consciousness and judgment as a person, and living naturally without the help of medical devices. Under that definition, an individual in the state of brain death is no longer "normally" alive. This is the medical rationale of those who define brain death as the death of a person. Human life is usually evaluated on the basis of cultural contribution, and those who are robbed of their ability to think by serious illness are often called "comatose" or a "vegetable." (I would note here that plants have no nervous system and do not think, though they have excellent physiological reactions that enable them to preserve their lives.)

When someone dies, they cannot be cremated or interred within 24 hours of certification of death by a doctor. When a person undergoes cardiac arrest, it does not mean that all the cells in the body die instantly— some are still alive. The biology of the human body is not my specialty, so I do not know if all the cells become completely dead within 24 hours or not, but it has probably been empirically verified that a human cannot be revived after 24 hours following cardiac arrest. However, the fact that cardiac arrest does not mean that all the cells that form the individual die instantly is noteworthy when it comes to brain death.

What happens if I remove some of my body cells and culture them in vitro? Cultured cells, if managed well with today's advanced technology, may live longer than cells in the body. In the meantime, I, as an individual, will eventually die. If the cells removed from my body are still alive in a culture, then who are they? If technology that could produce a cloned person from a human somatic cell existed, a complete human individual could be produced from that cultured cell. A copy of me could be created after I died. Who would that person be? Would I be resurrected after dying once as an individual? If a clone was created from a cell taken from my body, would that be me? It would be certainly possible to create an individual that has a DNA sequence identical to mine.

Every individual is unique, however, having been raised in an environment that has been historically unique since the moment when the fertilized egg—the starting point of an individual—begins to cleave. This is not at all like producing a device with a mold. Living things, even during the process of generation, respond and adapt to their habitat flexibly. Even monozygotic twins, which are two individuals that originated with a single cell, and hence have an identical DNA sequence, are not completely identical. They each have unique individuality. It is not possible to grow up through temporal—that is, historical—processes that are completely identical.

Therefore, even if a clone was made from one of my cells, it would be impossible to create an individual completely identical to me, even if it might be possible to create one that was extremely similar. That extremely similar clone would not be me, but a different person with a distinct individuality. Human life in particular, unlike that of other species, entails intellectual activities. A larger part of intelligence is acquired through education in the process of growing up than is expressed in information contained by the genes of living things. That is, intelligence is gained more from what is accumulated in society, outside of the individual's body, than what is engrained in its DNA as biological information. Therefore, even a clone that is quite similar to me in terms of human traits would have a different individuality as a person through totally different processes of generation and growth.

In nature, it is not at all a surprising or rare phenomenon for a plant with a different individuality to be cloned from the original one. Indeed, no one would regard a newly created cloned plant individual as the same individual as the parent. If we understand that it is a phenomenon common to living things that an organism generated and raised from one cell forms a new generation, the cloned individual is nothing but an independent individual of a new generation. This is even more the case for people; we seek human dignity—unseen among other organisms—in intellectual activities, so an individual of a new generation, even if cloned, is a completely new individual.

Brain death does not cause all the cells in the body to die immediately. The life of the individual that is unified by the brain may be only temporarily and artificially maintained, but the individual cells that form the individual are still alive. Those cells may not demonstrate the ability to develop into a complete organism (totipotence) under natural conditions, but it has been suggested that it is not impossible to create a cloned person if the technology is established. If we removed a cell from the brain of someone who was in the state of brain death and produced a clone, it would be possible to raise another person who had the same DNA sequence as the original. Yet that clone would be a different individual, independent from the one in the brain-dead condition. It would be the birth of a new individual, not the resurrection of the brain-dead person.

Deliberations on the Organ Transplant Law created a stir in Japanese society for their discussion of whether or not to recognize brain death as human death; the question was whether or not a person is alive when they have a physiological response in an artificially controlled state. From another angle, it was debated whether ending a life maintained by artificial devices, which are contrary to nature, would go against the law of nature—i.e., divine providence.

Most of us will not die a natural death, completing our individual life naturally. We have preventive medicine and medical treatment for diseases, and now it is even possible to keep the heart beating in cases where it would have meant death back when *Homo sapiens* was a wild species, not a person with culture. We determine when to shift from life to death artificially. Of course, this is a great blessing for people who want to live. We should be grateful for human progress in medicine and medical treatment. This nonetheless invites discussions like those that arose in the deliberations on the Organ Transplant Law. How should we regard artificial interventions that disrupt a death that should be dignified? There is no logical rationale for regarding the lives of individuals that are already extended by artificial means as being the same as life in the wild. When it reaches this level, maybe it is just a matter of preference whether we want to remain in a simulated state of living or not.

In some ways, people have become far removed from nature by developing artificiality. Even a person's lifespan is regarded as an individual matter. This is different from other species' stance on lifespans. Of course, many higher animals appear deeply concerned with the lives of individuals in the same community or those closely related to them. A conspicuous example is animals licking others' wounds to heal them. In such cases, however, they do not turn to highly advanced solutions that can be called medical acts. The artificiality that humans utilize represents a level of accumulated intelligence that is markedly different from that of other species' technologies. It is an undeniable fact that humans are special beings that possesses culture and civilization, though they are living organisms—this is common knowledge. Yet, we often confuse human beings as primates of the family Hominidae with people whose culture and civilization are highly advanced intellectual assets. Is this because we are still unable to depart from the idea that people are, after all, one species of animal?

I am alluding here to brain death as it relates to the social concept of the death of a human being, especially with respect to medical treatments like organ transplants. A person's life represents a particular activity in human culture, and it continues to influence society even after the physiological life has ended. This topic of the cultural life of human beings will be discussed later in this book.

Are individuals expendable?
Organisms live their lives, carrying on a life that has existed for over three billion years in life-forms that are recognized as individuals. They are aggregates of an astronomical number of atoms. Yet these atoms are replaced by others of the same element at such a tremendous speed that hardly any atom will remain in the same life-form for a whole year. Even so, we recognize life-forms as individuals, and we are aware of their births and deaths. In view of this, what does the life span of an individual mean?

The life of an individual organism ends in death. It starts when the new organism is born as a result of procreation—that is, at the beginning of a new generation. This is simple for organisms that reproduce sexually; a new individual is generated when two germ cells combine to form a zygote. (This is called a fertilized egg if the two gametes are an ovum [egg] and a sperm cell.) This is the prevailing type of sexual reproduction among higher animals and plants. The new individual inherits two different sets of genes from the parents; in the case of ovum and sperm cell, a male, or father, and a female, or mother. These two sets, though they belong to the same species as the parents, contain combinations of genes that are completely new, forming a new individual that has never existed on Earth before. This is the case for every new individual that is produced, even among the same species.

Focusing on the human race, we can distinguish between the self and others because every individual person has characteristics unique to them; that is, their individuality. We know that every person, including ourselves, will die after a time. The lifespan is the duration of time from an individual's birth to their death. An individual's life and death delineate its lifespan, rather than the life and death of its life. Therefore, we quite naturally understand the question about the length of our life to refer to our age as individuals.

That is to say, an individual has a limited life; it is a life-form that is entrusted with life for one generation. When the event of reproduction brings about generational change, life is given to another new individual; yet life is not generated here. Life goes on, secure in the individuals that inherit it; they are vehicles of life. Life replaces those individual organisms with new ones, staying youthful constantly—indeed, for over three billion years. It will continue to exist infinitely into the future. It may not be possible to ensure permanence of life without transferring it from one life-form to another through the occasion of reproduction. Individual life-forms are in themselves complete, and yet, as the vehicles of life, they are expendable in a way, something for life to pass through; just as atoms, which constitute life-forms, do not remain in the same organism. Life maintains its permanence, replacing the atoms and individual organisms on which it depends for existence with new ones.

How individuals influence the spherophylon after death

We learn a lot from the people who are no longer alive. Human culture is composed of a gigantic amount of information which has been accumulated over the course of human history. This includes all the information created by ourselves as well as by those who came before us. Our knowledge is based on information created by all human beings, present and past.

We are greatly affected, for instance, by the classics of Shakespeare, Goethe, and so on, music composed by Mozart, Beethoven, and so on, scientific contributions by Newton, Einstein, and so on, philosophy thought by Aristotle, Kant, and so on. None of us has ever met Aristotle (384–322 BCE) or Dante Alighieri (1265–1321 CE), though we learn from them in various ways, through the works they have left behind as well as exposure to them through our teachers. None of them are alive now. Yet our culture has preserved their cultural contributions, and we have free access to the heritage left by their knowledge and genius. In this way, humans can influence society even after their death. That our activities can continue even after the body is dead and buried is a special feature of human culture.

We benefit not only from the legacies of great geniuses, but also from those of the common people around us. The impact varies with the person concerned, though everyone influences those around them to some extent. We usually remember the suggestions of, for example, a grandmother or a childhood leader who often told us how kids should act—often with regret after not following their advice. We carry such memories not only from the seniors in the family but from various teachers, friends, students, and so on. In most cases, we do not realize where we gained this knowledge. Still, other people are the source of much of our knowledge, including those we have never seen and those who are no longer living.

From this fact, we can understand that our life is completed when our body ends the activity of living, but it also continues even after our body is gone. In this sense, an individual human life is endless, and will end only when the life of the spherophylon ends.

Organisms do not live alone; they all have various ties to one another. This means that every individual organism has a direct or indirect relationship with the others, and these relationships will exert various influences on each other. Even for organisms that have no culture, an individual life will continue to exert influence even after death of their bodies.

CHAPTER
2

✦

BIODIVERSITY: LIFE INTEGRATED ON EARTH BEYOND TIME AND SPACE

1. Species Diversity: How Much Do We Know about Species?

The current state of biodiversity research

It is a fact that the organisms on Earth as a whole have lived for billions of years thanks to their success in having various diverse features. At the Convention on Biological Diversity, adopted at the UN Conference on Environment and Development at Rio de Janeiro in 1992, diversity of organisms was recognized at three levels: genetic diversity, species diversity, and diversity of ecosystems. Since that time, biological diversity has mostly been discussed in terms of these three levels. In biology, however, various aspects of diversity are examined in the pursuit of a definition of life.

Diversity is an abstract concept describing the variance of characteristics in creatures. As it is invisible, it is not easy to explain to the general public. Unfortunately, there are not many people who even know the word "biodiversity."

In observing the life of the spherophylon, we recognize that this living existence has a near-infinite life span, having already lived for nearly four billion years, and a very wide living area covering the entire surface of Earth.

It can be said that people have made quite a bit of progress in deciphering phenomena by physicochemical analysis. Based on that knowledge, technology has also made substantial advancements. Our civilization is more radiant than ever before in the history of the human race, supported by the development of science and technology. The reductionist analysis of physicochemical phenomena was indeed a great scientific achievement. Unfortunately, we have to admit that much is still unknown, even in now in the twenty-first century, when it comes to natural phenomena, such as the facts about the planet and the cosmos, and organisms living on Earth.

Recent developments in biotechnology have benefited human society greatly. However, biodiversity, which can be even said to be a natural phenomenon in itself, has yet to be wholly unraveled, as research in this area is making slow progress. Though knowledge of biodiversity has been acquired to some extent as analytical technology in biological science developed, basic knowledge remains incomplete. We are keenly aware that we are far from uncovering the reality of biodiversity.

The number of extant species on Earth

About 1.8 million species have been described and recognized by biologists. As it is extremely difficult to list all these species, no one can tell the accurate number of currently recognized species with certainty. The figure of 1.8 million species, which is accepted by most biologists, is derived by roughly summing up the number of species recognized in each group and area and getting the grand total of those figures (table 2).

This estimate of 1.8 million species is a tremendous number; it represents the current status of biodiversity that a cohort of biologists surveyed every corner on the planet to uncover, spanning over 2,000 years from the age of Aristotle to the present day. Saying 1.8 million may not quite convey the magnitude of the number, but what if you named all the species one by one—for example, chimpanzee, mountain gorilla, lowland gorilla, orangutan . . . ? If you spent one second for each species, and did it for eight hours a day, five days a week, it would take about ten weeks to finish naming all the species. Ten weeks just to list their names! To learn what kind of creatures they are and try to grasp the characteristics of each one, we would have to multiply those hours many times over. Furthermore, even specialists have difficulty telling species apart. Thus, 1.8 million already recognized species is a bewilderingly large number.

Even this figure, though, is still very limited compared to the total number of species actually inhabiting Earth. An attempt at an experimental estimate of extant species on the planet was conducted in the late twentieth century in South America. This effort, which involved collecting and identifying all the organisms living in an area of approximately four hectares, showed that described species were only one seventh of the total, suggesting that the number of species on Earth is no fewer than 12 million—seven times the number of recognized species. This was followed by various other attempts to determine an estimate of the number of species living on Earth.

Of all the 1.8 million recognized species, the most numerous belong to the group of insects; insects alone account for over 800,000 (= 0.8 million) species, the majority of the total. Even with such a huge number of insect species already discovered, this group still holds many more unknown

Table 2 Numbers of extant species on Earth: recognized and estimated (thousands)

Taxon	Recognized	Estimated
Animals	1,400	
Vertebrates	60	
Invertebrates	1,300	13,000–103,000
Inc. insects	800	5,000–50,000
Inc. nematoda	15	5,000–50,000
Protozoa	30	100
Plants	275	300–500
Spermatophytes	220	
Pteridophytes	10	
Bryophytes	18	
Inc. algae	27	60
Fungi	47	1,500
Bacteria	7	30
Total	**About 1,800**	**?**

Sources: Various

species, and every survey unearths many new ones, especially in the tropics. In a survey conducted in a certain place in Central America, all the insects in a specific area were collected, from tree canopies to underground, by spraying chemicals, to compare the number of known and unknown species. Based on that ratio, it was estimated that 25 million species of insects alone lived in the tropical Americas. If 25 million species lived in this region, then, it could be roughly said that 50 million species existed on Earth.

There is a group of animals called nematodes that is divided into various species, despite their simple appearance. Currently, about 15,000 species are recognized. Some of them are parasitic, such as roundworms, which are parasitic to humans, and pinewood nematodes, or pine weevils, which are parasites on conifers. Parasites exist across all creatures and are classified into different parasitic species according to the host species (the organisms they are parasitic on). Following on this, it is estimated that number of species of parasitic nematodes is the same as the number of species of other groups living on Earth. If, for example, there are 50 million species of insects, it is estimated that there are 50 million species of nematodes parasitic to insects. There are free-living nematodes; many live in the sea, but they are minuscule. Specialists say that about 50 species of nematodes can be easily recognized in 10 milliliters of marine sediment. This means that tens of millions of nematode species inhabit Earth.

Fungi comprise another group about which not much of its diversity is known. Many species of soil bacteria can be recognized in a clod of earth, for example. Currently, a mere 47,000 species are recognized, but it is commonly held that no fewer than 1.5 million species exist (table 2).

The deep sea has long been dark in science, and species biologists used to believe that few species lived there. Recent observations in the deep sea, however, have revealed a diversity of organisms there. In addition, a great number of microbes have been observed around the hydrothermal vents in deep sea. Unknown types of evolution may be occurring there, and further investigation is sorely needed. Additional species diversity is anticipated in this area of observation.

The dearth of information on species diversity on Earth does not mean that research is lacking in all groups of animals and plants. It is estimated that for highly visible plants and vertebrates except fish, enough species are recognized to almost convey the whole picture. As for seed plants, approximately 250,000 species have been recognized so far, but the actual number of species is 300,000 by a conservative estimate, 500,000 by a generous one. Rather than assuming that all of these additional species are unknown, it is estimated that currently recognized species will be subdivided; the difference in estimates here comes from the range of anticipated subdivisions based on differences within a species.

In any event, as these examples make clear, there are, in fact, over 100 million species of extant organisms currently living on Earth. Naturally, it is not possible to provide an empirically accurate number, as estimates deal with what is actually unknown. Some question the rationale of the estimates. It is hard to defend the figure when asked if it was definitely only one out of seven species that was identified in the South American survey, and if the estimate was absolutely correct that there are 25 million species in Latin America alone based on identification of insects in a certain area. Rather than risking unreasonably large figures, scientists nowadays would say, "There must be as many as 10 million species," or "There must be at least 7 million extant species." It is risky to demand accuracy in these figures, but it cannot be doubted that there are more uncatalogued species than catalogued ones inhabiting Earth. The simple fact is that our current science knows so little about the actual number of extant species that estimates range from a few million to over 100 million.

In 2011, UNEP reported their estimate of the number of species on Earth; although general estimates of the number of extant species at that time was between 3 million and a few hundred million, UNEP compiled the information available and concluded that some 8.7 million species actually lived on Earth: 7.77 million animals, 298,000 plants, and 611,000 fungi, or 6.5 million terrestrial and 2.2 million marine species; of these, 86 percent of terrestrial species and 91 percent of marine species were still unknown to science.

Analysis of species diversity

Estimates of predicted species vary widely, not only because no one knows the number with any certainty, but also because people have different ideas about the species that are being counted. As mentioned earlier, there are 300,000 plant species by a conservative estimate, which is nearly doubled by a more ambitious one of 500,000. In general, floras are fairly well surveyed; still, the exact number of all plant species is not yet known.

While species are the basic unit demonstrating biodiversity, they also actually exist in nature, and so revealing their real condition is the most basic and important research theme in biology. This unit, unlike grams or centimeters, is not an artificial yardstick that can be adjusted. This is one reason for the difficulty in using physicochemical logic to understand diverse organisms in nature (a difference of approach is also apparent between the pursuit of laws and principles and the study of actual natural phenomena).

Cells and individuals are visible entities and thus easy to recognize. Species, however, are aggregates of numerous individuals, and therefore not easily differentiated. With sexually reproducing organisms, it is easy to understand, theoretically, that a unit that retains mutations and evolves is not a collection of individuals but a sexually reproducing group. Yet sexually reproducing groups (which exist as regional populations in reality) do not have as strong a presence as a unit as cells and individuals do. Even so, species do have a way of life, just as individuals do. This may become clear when we think about human life: there is definitely such a thing as the life of a human being. Furthermore, no human being is identical to another individual; this is common to all creatures. Each species has its specific characteristics and contains unique variations; this is one of the most vital, universal principles of living organisms, or carriers of life.

Modern science gives a provisional definition of species as a hypothesis. Researchers interpret this hypothesis in their own ways, and make distinctions between species according to their own standards. This is not to say, of course, that individual researchers are being irresponsible. The grand total of 1.8 million known species is widely regarded as common knowledge in biology, as there is a general consensus regarding the concept of species, based on current biological knowledge and insight. Even so, some variance may be acceptable, since much about the nature of organisms has yet to be revealed. Scientists anticipate greater understanding will reveal greater complexity, and species will be subdivided further. This means that there is a wide range of estimates even for plant species, which are relatively well known.

How much do we know about each of the 1.8 million named species? In fact, for a staggering number of them all we have are the characteristics that were described when they were first introduced as new species. Only in a handful of cases has the structure of the species been analyzed biologically, at least with respect to their phenomena, which is a very limited part of everything to be known about that species. Remember that our knowledge about *Homo sapiens*—our own species—is still insufficient; for instance, we are affected by a variety of diseases which cannot be cured even at present.

Improvements in biological research techniques have made it relatively easy to understand the structure of DNA; that is, its base sequence, which controls the hereditary traits of species. These are determined by differences in the sequence of the four kinds of bases in DNA: adenine, cytosine, guanine and thymine. Therefore, once we learn all the base sequences, we will be able to get at what determines the individual traits of species. For example, if we unlock the entire base sequence of human DNA, it will provide knowledge that is useful for medicine and other fields. For this reason, the Human Genome Project (HGP; note that the genome is a set of genes in an organism) was launched with a massive research budget, mobilizing researchers and engineers throughout the world with state-of-the-art devices.

Now, given rapid technical development, we may obtain all the DNA sequences for many species, including humans, but we still would have to say that the number of species completely sequenced is limited in view of all the species extant on Earth. Sequencing only tells us the structure of DNA; further study is needed to understand how it produces the organism's characteristic traits, and how such traits are harnessed in daily life. If it takes so much energy to reveal the forms and characteristics of one species, what would it be like to attempt to understand all the traits of millions or tens of millions of species? What would it be like to understand the entire picture of the life of the spherophylon, beyond time and space?

We have, indeed, made known various phenomena that are regarded as universal, surrounding what it means to live. Yet, when it comes to knowledge of biodiversity, what information we have acquired is a tiny portion of the whole. We must realize that clearly in exploring how we live today.

The concept of biological species

The species diversity of organisms can be measured using species as a unit. However, this is a biological unit completely unlike physicochemical units such as gram for weight and meter for length. In contrast to those clearly defined units, species is a standard that reflects the realities of organisms that exist in various forms on Earth.

When John Ray (1627–1705) first used species as a concept to describe differences between organisms, he distinguished species by visible differences in specific characteristics. Carl Linnaeus (1707–1778), who established an organism classification system in the eighteenth century, defined species basically using the same approach as Ray did; he described all the living things known to him, and created the binominal nomenclature for naming species. In the middle of the nineteenth century, Charles Darwin (1809–1882) proposed an idea that would be later called the theory of evolution, from the point of view that species are evolving entities. When the study of genetics became advanced in the twentieth century, the characteristics of species were studied from the perspective of genetics, with differences between species defined in terms of differences in genetics. Further, as molecular science progressed, it became known that some differences between species can be interchangeable with the degree of difference in DNA. Therefore, the term "species" was understood on a different level in the seventeenth century than it is today.

As a unit, a species does not comprise organisms that are simply aggregates of similar individuals. Sexually reproducing organisms form regional populations that are interbreedable; this is the basic concept of biological species proposed by Ernst Mayr (1904–2005; Mayr, 1942). Species not only have a specific structure, but also live as a species and as a unit that undergoes evolution. This distinction makes the biological characteristics of a species distinct from its individual life-maintaining mechanisms. Species represent the basic unit that demonstrates the biodiversity arising out of the evolution of living things over a long period of time.

To say this, however, requires objective understanding and a definition of species as a unit. In an obvious example, some propose that genetic differences between species and the rates of successful crossbreeding should be used as the standards in measuring differences between species. Yet it is not possible to apply the definition for sexually reproducing populations directly to asexual populations, and it is extremely difficult to come up with a biologically universal definition of species or taxon (in a limited number of words) to include creatures that take different forms of existence. Furthermore, given the limited amount of information available on species, having an objective definition of the term may prove to be erroneous.

The species of living things is not a convenient unit for discussing biodiversity; rather, it is a topic of research that should be central to biological study. It is only when biology explains everything that we can arrive at a biologically correct definition of this particular term.

2. Genetic Diversity

The diversity of organisms has been summarized at the level of species in the preceding section. Biodiversity, however, has additional aspects.

It has already been noted that each species is a comprehensive composite of various individuals, with no individual being completely the same as another. Every individual is distinct from all the other individuals of the same species. This individual variation is introduced by genetic biodiversity.

The structure and function of DNA

The genetic diversity of organisms can be explained by the nature of genetic substances—principally DNA. DNA (an abbreviation for deoxyribonucleic acid) is a biopolymer commonly found in organisms. Deoxyribose and phosphoric acids form long chains of molecules, combined with four kinds of bases—adenine, guanine, thymine and cytosine—and two of those chains of molecules twist together to form the double helix structure.

The molecules in DNA carry genetic codes for the development, functioning, growth, and reproduction of organisms and viruses. The structure and diversity of the DNA molecule arise from the four bases which are arranged in sequence on polynucleotide chains.

Depending on the sequence of the four bases, innumerable kinds of molecules can be created. It is not necessary to go into the details of these chemical structures; suffice it to say that these molecules serve as a template to create molecules with an identical structure, as if they are mirrored—they have the ability to self-replicate. Its diverse structure—which is determined by the sequence of the four bases—and its self-reproducing feature allow DNA to pass on the specific traits of an organism from a mother cell to a daughter cell—from the parent generation to the child's generation. Therefore, it plays the part of the life-delivering gene. As DNA thus communicates complex information accurately, it maintains and produces features of organisms that are historically consistent.

Another nucleic acid called RNA (ribonucleic acid) is produced within the cell according to the base sequence, and specific proteins are produced according to the RNA's base sequence. As protein is the basic molecule that determines an organism's functions, specific protein groups are produced, forming a distinctive life-form that closely resembles the parent.

DNA is able to accurately replicate molecules with identical structures to its own, using itself as a template. That is how it plays its part in genes and why the biological phenomenon is established that is summarized by the saying, "Of a thorn springs not a fig." Yet all biological phenomena have exceptions. DNA's self-reproduction, which is supposed to be infallible, does—though very rarely—make the mistake of copying the base sequence inaccurately. This is called gene mutation. The frequency of mutation for extant organisms is about once in a million times to once in hundred million times, though it varies depending on the species or tissues. Mutations occur quite randomly in nature—neutrally, in other words.

Certain types of chemicals, cosmic rays, and radiation rays can trigger mutations that are not natural. This only affects the frequency of mutation, not the particular direction or selection of mutation. Recent technological advances have made it possible to induce specific mutations artificially. The biotechnology, usually called genetic recombination, has been widely applied in recent biological research, as well as in the realms of agricultural and veterinary technology.

Biodiversity happens in the world of organisms based on a certain ratio of neutral mutation within DNA molecules. DNA molecules duplicate themselves, and a certain ratio of variation is introduced in the process of duplication. This means that DNA, which is a higher molecule with long chain, usually contains variations, though naturally DNA of a certain species has a fixed construction specific to that species. Through such genetic variations, it is DNA that causes organisms to evolve. This started when the first living thing appeared on Earth and supported the existence of living thing there. Mutations in the DNA led to genetic diversity, and genetic diversity led to the evolution of organisms which supported life on Earth in the billions of years.

The genetic laws of inheritance
As previously noted, molecules are not alive in and of themselves, but the cells that contain them are alive. What is the difference here? Cells reproduce through a particular process (cell division) common to organisms. Molecules, however (except for DNA in certain situations), cannot reproduce themselves, even when they contain the same proportion of

elements as cells. A particular morphological structure is established to form a living cell, though the details are still unknown to science. Life is passed down from the parents to the children of the next generation to through the reproductive process.

Organisms have particular morphological structures whose functions are specific to each species. These features are inherited through a fixed process via reproduction. This particular phenomenon is usually explained under the term "heredity."

Heredity is defined as a phenomenon where specific features such as body shape and color are passed on from parents to children and grandchildren, and from a cell to the next generation of cells, which is governed by communication of genes and their expressions. This phenomenon is specific to living organisms, and is their most conspicuous feature. The substances actually inherited by daughter cells from their mother cell are the chromosomes, and it is known that DNA is the last substance that is passed down to the succeeding generation. Actually, DNA can reproduce itself using the mother molecule as a template. Based on these facts, DNA is considered the substance responsible for genetics.

When organisms communicate genetic information etched into their DNA to the next generation correctly, that information will have specific structures and functions. The features of various structures and functions are contained in a specific system of genes, preserved through the DNA's self-replicating process; they produce protein through RNA, which forms a living creature according to the information communicated by the DNA. That DNA is communicated to the next generation via reproduction. It is through this hereditary mechanism that life-forms are able to accurately pass life on through history. Life has been constantly passed down within a closed system of life-forms. When traced back, this inevitably leads to the moment when life occurred. Life became a historical existence because the hereditary mechanism was established.

Gregor Mendel (1822–1884), from the modern-day Czech Republic, established the laws of heredity, although his findings were ignored by academia for 35 years after publication. Also, there is a dark history surrounding the USSR's intervention into science to suppress his study of genetics. Nonetheless, biology became established as one area of modern science by studying genetics, analyzing it by physiochemical techniques, and making life the object of reductionist study.

3. Biodiversity: Diverse Phenomena Found in Living Things

Ecological diversity
All living things live by adapting to their environments. Each species has its own life form, and each individual in any species has its own way of living. Still, no individual can live without collaborating with other individuals.

The organisms on Earth have their living activities: eating, breathing, moving, metabolism, growth, reproduction, etc., mostly by their own efforts, though every activity requires them to collaborate with the other organisms. Animals inhale oxygen and emit carbon dioxide; in return, plants absorb carbon dioxide and emit oxygen while they carry out photosynthesis. For sexual reproduction, individuals of the opposite sex form pairs, even in the case of monoecious plants. Animals eat inorganic substances, but mainly consume organisms and their byproducts; and fungi are usually parasitic or saprophytic (consuming decayed organisms), or are mycotrophic (living in partnership with each other)—and the list goes on. Without the help of other organisms, living things cannot sustain life.

Every living thing has its own relationship to particular individuals of the same species and to the other species. For all the organisms on Earth, under proper equilibrium, such relationships are established to form a global biosphere, and this collaborative system is evident in the form of an ecosystem.

An ecosystem is established when organisms adapt to the environmental conditions in a particular place. The tremendous variety of ecosystems show another phase of biodiversity. To recognize the diversity of ecosystems, we classify geographical regions according to flora and fauna, classify the types of vegetation, and draw up a variety of ecosystems in local areas. Here, we will further discuss the range of ecological biodiversity that has been observed, which shows the mutual collaboration organisms engage in to sustain their living activities.

The characteristics of living things vary

The term biodiversity (an abbreviation of "biological diversity") was proposed in the 1980s, becoming more widely known following the adoption of the Convention on Biological Diversity in 1992. Since then, biodiversity has been taken up as a topic on one of three levels—genetic diversity, species diversity, and ecological diversity—especially in the context of environmental issues.

Diversity is more widely observed in various phenomena in biology, or organisms are usually treated as a conglomerate of diversity. Living organisms continue living as they maintain their diversity in various ways. The diversity of biological phenomena is evident in the morphology and function of various organic substances, cells, tissues, organs, and individuals, in various elements of a variety of taxa, in various ecosystems, and so on. Every part is different in age and historical background (phylogeny), depending on the organism in question.

Rather than enumerating the diversity of organisms, here we will show a typical example in the case of a cell. Cell diversity is evident in the number of different types of cells: nervous cells, epidermal cells, mesenchyme cells, muscle cells, blood cells, egg cells, sperm cells, and so on for the multicellular animals (metazoa). Vascular plants have epidermal cells, stomatal cells, spongy tissue cells, palisade tissue cells, xylem cells, xylem parenchyma cells, phloem cells, phloem parenchyma cells, fibrous tissue cells, egg cells, pollen, spores, and so on; other organisms have a variety of other kinds of cells. Rather than enumerating the variety of morphological units, would simply ask readers to consider how diverse biological phenomena are.

The most significant point of biological diversity may be referenced here. The life of organisms has been maintained now for nearly 40 trillion years thanks to this biological diversity. When life on Earth was created—either originating there or introduced from a star—the first action of that life-carrying body was to produce variation, actually creating variants of DNA molecules in a certain frequency. (There is a hypothesis that the original organism inherited its life through RNA; if this was the case, it would have created variation in its RNA.) When DNA molecules multiply through self-reproduction, they usually produce accurate copies, though errors occur once in a million to a hundred million times on average.

If organisms have no variation, what will happen to them? Organisms normally sustain life as they adopt to their environment on Earth. The environment is not stable, however, and is changing constantly. Environmental change can prove intolerable to certain organisms, and these species become endangered and then extinct over time. If any species subject to unexpected environmental change has variants in its population, and any of those variants can tolerate the new environment and continue living, those variants can survive even if most of their colleagues die. The life that they continue to sustain is maintained by having diversity in its population, so the variants are able to survive through inevitable environmental changes.

If DNA were always accurately replicated without variation, all organisms would have the same morphology and function, resembling extremely elaborate industrial products. These organisms might live efficiently, adapting to the environment they live in. If a change of environment were introduced, however, the organisms would not be able to adapt and survive; they would become endangered, then extinct, and life would end. Thus, diversity of organisms is one of the most basic and significant principles for maintaining life.

The diversity of organisms at various levels: DNA, cells, individuals, species, the ecosystem, and the spherophylon

Biodiversity can be observed in every dimension of living bodies. In researching diversity in species, we do not always look at the entire species. We examine organs and tissues in depth, even just to learn how diverse species are. Features are used to distinguish between different species, as long as they can be used as taxonomic keys to identify lower taxa. In the past, highly visible external features were often used to define species' characteristics, but we need features that express phylogenetic relationships more accurately if we want to understand how they are related to other species. A basic task of phylogenetic investigation is to select features to use as taxonomic keys.

Cells form the foundation of the structure of all organisms. They are a universal unit, yet in themselves they are extremely diverse. Prokaryotic cells and eukaryotic cells have fundamentally different structures. Even among eukaryotic cells, germ cells and somatic cells have clear differences in both their structure and functions. The cell structures of animals, plants, and fungi all are different; furthermore, in animal cells, the cells of the nerves, muscles, skin, bone marrow, and so on also differ. The term "cell" encompasses this great diversity of structure and function; therefore, organisms are naturally diverse, though their unit of life is the cell. Nevertheless, it is very helpful to use cells as a universal unit. The diversity of cells as a unit derives from the diversity of organelles as the unit that makes up cells, and also from the diversity of the molecules that form cells. The DNA contained in cells is also diverse, which contributes to species diversity at the gene level. Therefore, levels of diversity research range from species and higher taxa to DNA.

As I have explained, the process of living is a phenomenon that is demonstrated by cells, by individuals, and by the spherophylon. Talking about cells may sound like a very minute and intricate matter to a layperson, but the biology of cells requires an extremely integrative viewpoint, since cells are a single system made up of individual molecules and organelles. Individuals are made of numerous cells, which, as an aggregate, form specific structures and functions. This structure of independent units forming a system also applies to the spherophylon, which is on the scale of the entire planet. When it includes even the spherophylon, the sheer expanse of the structure seems vast and incomprehensible, however, making it difficult to know where to start.

What does deciphering the life of the spherophylon on Earth through biodiversity research entail? It absolutely requires an integrated perspective, as biodiversity research cannot be completed with a reductionist approach alone. In order to go into this, we need to discuss specific studies. Individual analytical studies should be pursued thoroughly for their own ends, but those goals should always be evaluated in relation to integration. I summarized my own efforts to do so in my book *The Natural History of Ferns* (Iwatsuki, 1997a). I do not mean to say that one scholar or one group must do everything, including analysis and integration. What is important here is to recognize how the object of analysis contributes to understanding what it means to live. That is what scientific research is about.

Pointlessly churning out research papers in a fashionable field may lead to small contributions to science. Furthermore, you may produce results using technology, but they may not necessarily contribute to development of science. Conversely, those who are clear-headed about what needs to be done cannot be said to contribute to science if they do not have technology or passion to produce analytical results.

It cannot be denied that biodiversity has become a theme in general scientific research, partly because it deserves to be fashionableere. Instead of simply discussing the matter with estimates, it has become possible to empirically analyze data, for anyone to clearly see how accurately research can be pursued. Yet if it ends here, now that it is discussed in a language common to sciences, there is a risk that biodiversity research may not help bring to light the phenomenon of the spherophylon, which has a nearly infinite expanse. If what is intended to be an analysis of diversity is limited to an analysis of the phenomena that researchers are concerned with, they are following in the footsteps of those who were criticized for taking a fanatical interest in the similarities and differences between organisms.

Biodiversity research contributes to the analysis of the universal principles of living, while it also deciphers the various ways in which organisms live. We cannot analyze diverse phenomena if we are content to merely say they are diverse. In order to understand them, we need to decide on a model for analysis; yet a model is nothing but a model, not the entire phenomenon of living. We must not forget it is only a small part of the whole. The whole, here, refers to the entity of life with a history of over three billion years, as I have repeatedly explained. Life creates history, and is swayed by the history it has created. History holds a tremendous amount of information. At every point in history, localized necessities of the moment accumulate, forming the entirety of history. The reality arising out of this history is the spherophylon that exists on Earth at this moment. Biology aims to close in on the entity of this life, and the biology of diversity intends to understand what it means to live in the unit of the spherophylon. Our current scientific logic and methods cannot decipher all of history. Obviously, the biology of diversity is not a subject that can be understood without an integrative view.

4. The Phylogeny of Living Organisms

Organisms differentiating into myriad types

Living things age. Their age can be the length of the history of life they contain, or the duration of time that the substances forming their individual life-form remain in it, or the individual's age. Whether or not replacing life's age with the individual's age or lifespan is applicable to organisms in general should be considered in relation to the definition of individuals, as discussed in chapter 1. Here, let us explore how the life you possess, which is over three billion years old, is connected with the life of other creatures. In other words, if our life has an origin that dates incomparably further back than the beginning of our individual existence, through what historical journey has it become ours?

The first moment of life on Earth has not yet been precisely established. Recently, however, it is acknowledged that the monophyletic theory, which holds that life on Earth started from a unique type, is regarded as almost certain. Living things arrived at their present diversity by repeating divergence, or so-called evolution, over the course of the three-billion-year history of life. In other words, they may be different, but they can be traced back to the same type, because myriad types have been generated from a single prototype. For example, as in figure 1, all the living creatures on Earth share historical processes converging at the same source in the form of a phylogenetic tree, much like a family tree. When tracing back the history of evolution—of the human race, for example—the organisms assumed a monkey shape a few million years ago. Going hundreds of million years further back, they had a fish-like form; finally, three billion years ago, all creatures looked like bacteria. This is a fact that most biologists now acknowledge. It applies not just to humans: all organisms on Earth—monkeys, fish, and colon bacilli—converge into the same life-form when traced back more than three billion years.

Principles resulting in biodiversity

Much has been revealed about the process of diversification. Evolution is triggered by genetic mutations, which are accidental changes that occur at a certain rate. With most organisms, these mutations are maintained and dispersed within sexually reproducing populations, leading to the formation of separate species. This has been studied theoretically, and has been observed in actual cases. The idea that evolution takes place in the unit of populations has nearly been proven as a theory. Populations are part of the spherophylon that has been nurtured through history, and evolution corrects part of the spherophylon; this means that evolution cannot be a phenomenon that makes radical modifications to the spherophylon.

If genetic data controls the form and functions of individuals that form a population, the phenomena of cladogenesis—where one species diverges into two or more—and of anagenesis—where one species turns into a different one—can be understood as the modification of genetic information through the same universal principles. Yet understanding the principles does not solve the mystery of evolution. It is not impossible to trace how the principles work on organisms which are now living; even so, the processes of evolution are different for, say, humans and wild cherries, and not all of them have been identified yet.

Whether as individuals or as species, all extant organisms live as part of the spherophylon, which has been created by evolution. Every single phenomenon produced by all the organisms on Earth over the past three billion years and more is included in the history of evolution. They are historical facts created by all organisms on a global scale. These phenomena are ongoing today. The present just reflects one aspect of the life of the spherophylon.

All organisms are related to each other
When we trace the history of how life-forms developed after they first emerged on the planet about three billion years ago, they first assumed a shape similar to bacteria, and then diverged into various forms of bacteria such as bacilli, spirochetes, cyanobacteria, and staphylococci. Whether one of these took the form of cyanobacteria or a spirochete determined its subsequent path as an organism. In a more familiar example, our fish-like ancestors of a few hundred million years ago separated into fish and human branches at some occasion. Those that happened to be in the latter group evolved into monkeys or people. You may have a certain assuredness about your birth as a human being, but your life is simply contained in a life-form that happens to have evolved into a human; you could have been a monkey screeching on a tree in the woods somewhere, depending on the path a life container took a few million years ago. You could even have been the beech or oak tree that the monkey is hanging onto, if you had taken a different path in the history of evolution over one billion years ago. Incidentally, if your life had taken the phylogenetic course to be a tuna, having selected different DNA some several hundred thousand years ago, you might be served as sashimi on your friend's dinner table tonight.

All living organisms, including the human race, are now diversified into multifarious species said to number over a hundred million, all related to each other through lines of evolutionary descent. This is quite similar to the way all the cells that form an individual animal or plant derive from one single fertilized egg, starting with cleavage, splitting into more

56

than a trillion cells in the case of human beings. The fact that life has history means that all the life-forms on this planet share interrelated lineages (phylons). Biodiversity signifies not just that Earth has an immense number of species, but that all those species are related to a single line—or a limited number of lines—of evolutionary descent.

CHAPTER

3

LIFE SUPPORTED BY SPACE: MUTUAL COLLABORATION BY
ALL THE ORGANISMS ON EARTH

1. How Complete Is an Individual in Its Life?

What is an individual?

When we think about what it means to live, we usually have our own lives in mind; it is in our nature that we are unable to ponder about life separately from our individual lives. This may help us understand life as an experience, but it poses a problem in that we may overlook the intrinsic nature of life that is common to diverse life-forms if we are bound by the form of our own individual lives.

Each of us lives as an individual organism. What are multicellular organisms, though? We need to consider the meaning of "individual." How far can we generalize our own existence to the life of organisms in general? In fact, we will learn that we cannot simply generalize human existence to various species, when we examine what it means for organisms to be alive.

It may be easier for us to understand the meaning of life for animal individuals. A new generation begins generally with fertilized eggs (fertilized egg = zygote); the universal phenomenon is that, through a process called development, they form gastrulas (a stage of embryonic development). differentiate germ layers, and form tissues and organs, developing into adult organisms. Individuality is more blurred for plants, however. Individual microorganisms are fairly different in form and function compared to individual animals and plants.

Fully developed, mature animal bodies are controlled by the nervous system. Plants, on the other hand, do not develop a similar system; rather, cells are arranged according to rules unique to the species. Furthermore, unlike animals, which have a finite lifespan, plants (except annual and biennial varieties) have unlimited life, as long as they can overcome the matter of physical support. This is because plants have the physical feature of repeating cellular differentiation in the meristem, just as animal embryos do. Meristems, or points of growth, are structures that generate new tissues and organs at the tips of the shoot and the roots. For example, giant sequoias (*Sequoiadendron giganteum*), known as the largest trees in the world, may be a few thousand years old, but they carry out cell division at the tips of the shoots and the roots, as lively as when they just sprouted. Cells that were born a few thousand years ago (now dead and become tissue) and baby-like newly grown cells coexist in an individual plant, giving it an infinite lifespan as an individual. Trees can live endlessly, as long as they can support their bodies.

It may be easy to think of an individual plant when we think about a single tree. But what about a bamboo grove? Bamboos have rhizomes, or underground stems. A single bamboo cane, which sprouts in spring as a bamboo shoot and grows at an extraordinary speed, is actually connected with other canes underground. Each cane is not, therefore, an individual, but equivalent to a single branch. A number of bamboo canes, connected by rhizomes, form a single individual. What happens if the rhizomes are cut, severing the connection? Two individuals will be created if the rhizome is cut in two, or five, if in five. Also, a cane cut off at the ground level and left there will die, but other canes connected via the rhizomes will not. The rest of the individual organism will live, though part of it is removed.

Such vegetative reproduction may be seen also in particular metazoa; it is often offered as an example of asexual reproduction. If you cut the body of an adult into two portions, both parts regenerate their lost half, becoming two seemingly perfect adult bodies. In this case, regeneration results in asexual reproduction. When cut off, the tail of a newt may regenerate naturally, though this is not analogous to vegetative reproduction, as the individual that results from this phenomenon is not perfect.

Somatic plant cells, not just meristems, have totipotency—the capacity to regenerate the whole plant from a cell—if certain conditions are met. Plant tissues are also highly regenerative. It is a common phenomenon that part of a plant, removed from the whole, regenerates into an independent plant; cutting and layering play an important part in gardening. Vegetative propagation is an ordinary phenomenon: cutting and removing plant tissues increases the number of individual plants. Propagation through runners is a trait of more than few plants, such as garden strawberries. Sweet potatoes are cultivated by cutting off and planting numerous young shoots from seed potatoes, depending on their regenerative power; regular potatoes, too, can produce large quantities when cut seed potatoes are planted in the field.

Organisms originally were single-celled. For unicellular organisms, cell division leads to an increase in the number of individuals. Cell division means proliferation and reproduction for them. In this sense, what is the meaning of "lifespan" for unicellular organisms? When DNA within a cell multiply and the cell doubles itself, it does not just double the number of cells—it erases the mother cell. This means that the mother cell has had its time. The composition of the cell is passed on to the next generation; this is how generational change, or the end of the parent's generation accompanied by procreation, is marked for unicellular organisms, though the mother cell does not leave a corpse behind. We remember here that no natural death of individuals is observed at this stage; or all the materials of the parent's generation are survived in the bodies of new generation.

Another example is what is called a colony. Some organisms live in colonies—groups of independent cells living together without establishing themselves as a multicellular organism—such as single-celled algae and protozoans. Cell relationships vary, from those simply living in a colony with hardly any cooperation, to volvoxes (a type of green algae) and others that form what could be called a social life of cells. These organisms become highly specialized as a colony, having separate roles of reproduction and photosynthesis and other activities for different cells.

Readers may not be terribly familiar with algae, but even those who have not viewed them through a microscope must have at least heard of *Chlorella* and *Chlamydomonas*, and some may remember them from figures in textbooks. These are single-celled examples. *Gonium* is another example; it resembles *Chlamydomonas*, but it lives in a colony of 4 to 16 cells. *Pandorina* lives in a colony of 16 to 32 cells. These algae lead a life comparable to individuals forming a society, as multiple single cells gather together though retaining independence (figure 2).

In zoology, the term "colony" is widely used for the state in which individual organisms newly generated by cell division or germination stay connected with the mother. This applies to creatures like hydrozoans and

Fig. 2 Colonial algae and hydroids

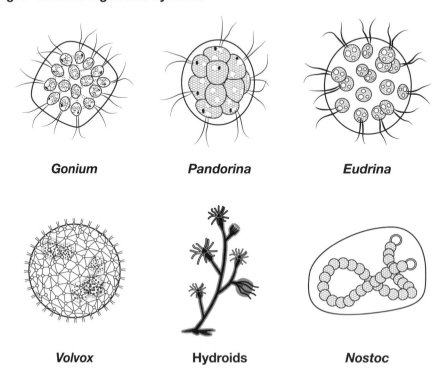

Gonium   Pandorina   Eudrina

Volvox   Hydroids   Nostoc

bryozoans. These differ from algae colonies in that they consist of multi-cellular individuals.

Even among colony-forming algae, *Gonium* and *Pandoria* are able to split all the cells forming the colony, so that each cell can independently form a new colony. *Eudorina* forms the largest colonies, with 32, 64, or 128 cells; some cells of *Eudorina* cannot start another colony if they are cut off from theirs.

Initially, the cells of such colonies take the form of a flat plate, with the flagella of the cells all extended in the same direction; when the number of cells forming the colony increases, however, they form a sphere, the most stable state, with the cells arranged on the surface, and are no longer able to take on a flat shape. *Volvox*, which has a much larger number of cells—from 500 to 60,000—forms a smooth, spherical colony. When as many as 10,000 cells gather, cells start to split into those that are dedicated to photosynthesis and those dedicated to reproduction, even though the colony remains a loose gathering of cells forming a community without becoming an organization.

Blue-green algae such as *Oscillatoria* and *Nostoc* form colonies in which the cells are arranged in filaments. These cells have certain mutual relationships to each other; they are not just arranged together. When separated, however, they will continue the colony independently; that is, if you cut one filament into two, you will have two independent colonies. Yet they have specially formed cells, such as those called heterocysts and akinetes; this demonstrates cell differentiation, even though they are not multicellular organisms.

By this definition, colonies are not multicellular organisms, nor are they in the process of evolving into them. They evolved specifically for this way of life. But it is also important to remember that multicellular organisms can live in colonies, too, when we examine the life of multicellular organisms as individual beings.

Prior to more than a billion years ago, unicellular organisms only proliferated by copying the parent (though it may also be a fact that prokaryotes, ancient organisms whose cells lack a nucleus, exchange genes between cells). In the meantime, some evolved into multicellular organisms, where multiple cells gather to form one individual. It is not clear whether multicellular organisms evolved first, or sexual reproduction began first. In any event, following the advent of multicellular organisms and sexual reproduction, organisms underwent amazing evolution in the complexity and sophistication of the composition of life-forms and the diversity of species. The human race is one example of a creature that evolved into a highly sophisticated life-forms through such a process. Therefore, individuality is more easily recognized for animals with established multicellularity—humans in particular—than for other organisms.

Among the topics that have been in the spotlight these days, there are two that give us insight into the significance of life: cloned sheep (discussed below) and brain death (discussed in chapter 1). Both matters pose the question of the meaning of life from a contemporary perspective. They are often discussed in relation to bioethics, but I will discuss them here with special emphasis on the life of the spherophylon.

The spherophylon and cloned sheep: a dream of a better life
Let us examine cloned sheep, made famous by the sheep Dolly (1996), from a biological perspective. With ordinary sheep, the starting point for a new generation is a fertilized egg made of the father's sperm and the mother's egg. This, called sexual reproduction, is a reproductive process common to animals. Yet a cloned sheep was created without going through this process. The researchers used the genes of ordinary somatic cells, rather than germ cells (sperm and egg); the resulting individual was named Dolly. In this case, the composition of the DNA from the parents' somatic cells was not modified, except in gene mutations during cell division, creating a clone whose genes were constituted identically to those of its parents. Usually, as a rule, an animal offspring born out of ordinary sexual reproduction has a new genetic composition that mixes genes from both parents.

The cloning of Dolly was a breakthrough for mammals, but the phenomenon is commonly used for plant reproduction. In fact, it is a popular technique in agriculture and gardening. Cloning, for plants, is an ordinary reproductive phenomenon. Plant cells are totipotent; in other words, every cell—not just reproductive cells—has the potential to express the reproductive capacity of genes to the fullest. A single plant cell has the genetic capability to create a multicellular individual identical to the parent.

The totipotency of plant cells was proven independently by Frederick C. Steward and Jakob Reinert in 1958, in separate experiments on generating whole carrots from a callus, or cell adhesion (when plant tissues are damaged, tissues that are active in cell division are induced and formed). Also, a group of Japanese researchers, led by Itaru Tatebe and Toshiyuki Nagata, demonstrated that an entire tobacco plant could be regenerated from a single protoplast; that is, the entire cell except the cell wall—a term for plants, whose cells have walls made of cellulose and hemicellulose— the equivalent of "cells" for animals.

When cell division begins in a single cell, which is the starting point for a plant, cytodifferentiation occurs in various tissues, forming various cells as the plant grows and becomes multicellular. However, not a single one of the somatic cells that make up the plant loses its totipotency. In botany, tissue culturing techniques are rapidly developing, contributing significantly to productivity in the agricultural and pharmaceutical fields.

For animals, in contrast, at a very early stage of the fertilization of a single cell, which is the starting point for multicellular individuals, functional and structural differences are established between the cells that preserve totipotency and eventually become germ cells, and the somatic cells devoted to forming the body and maintaining the life-form, which lose totipotency.

Animals' somatic cells lose mosaicism at an early stage. Immediately after cleavage starts in a fertilized egg, each cell has the potential to become an individual entity, but it loses that flexibility when its future is determined as the cleavage progresses. That is to say, only germline cells preserve totipotency, while others assume specific forms. The vast number of cells that constitute one life-form, a single individual, must have the same DNA sequence, except for differences due to very infrequent gene mutations. This is because an individual that started with a single cell becomes a multicellular life-form made of numerous cells via cell division, in which a process is repeated where the mother cell duplicates DNA accurately and splits them into two daughter cells. We can surmise that totipotency is not completely lost in animal somatic cells; it is simply suppressed so that it cannot be developed spontaneously. It is not impossible for a single somatic cell to generate a multicellular life-form, if we give it a little help to enable its DNA to express that capability. If this assumption is correct, with some outside manipulation animals should be able to demonstrate totipotency, which plants can do in natural state. Dolly's success meant that an experimental technology was developed to express the genes of a cell that has lost totipotency; the fact that this was achieved for a mammal made it sensational news.

There are stem cells that maintain the capacity for genetic domination, and particular utilization of stem cells is now a hot topic in the medical and veterinary fields. Medicinal technology developed the iPS cell, which enabled totipotent development of tissues and/or organs of animals without germline cells; it is anticipated that the regeneration of specific tissues and organs can be activated artificially by induced iPS cells.

Biologically speaking, cloning is already available as a useful technology for people. So why did the cloning of Dolly make headlines? For one thing, it raised the possibility of greater efficiency in meat and milk production. Above all, it is because it brought us closer to the possibility of this technology being applied to the human race, which has many similarities with sheep. The success of sheep-cloning technology led to a debate about the possibility of human cloning. Though only a few specialists discussed that possibility when carrots were cloned, and even when frogs were cloned by J. B. Gurdon in 1975, it was only natural to consider it when cloning was achieved for sheep. Here, we faced new issues surrounding the creation of a human being with exactly the same genetic makeup as another.

Sheep cloning was accepted as a successful new technology to improve agricultural and livestock production, which is beneficial for humankind. No one questions the cloning of garden strawberries from an ethical standpoint. When it comes to cloning sheep, however, some may bring up the issue of animal protection; then again, if we are to discuss that, we must first acknowledge that domestic animals, including pets, are placed in an unnatural state compared to wild animals and plants. In this book, I consistently argue that we need to predict potential dangers and take sufficient precautions when adopting a new technology so that it does not invite unexpected problems. We do not have enough information to evaluate the risk of sheep cloning triggering unknown hazards here. Even so, it is essential to apply new technologies for the purpose of pursuing human prosperity while limiting the usurpation of nature.

The success of the sheep-cloning trial suggests the possibility of cloning humans. In the realm of reproductive biology, research is done on a far greater scale for the human race compared to other primates. If it is possible to clone sheep, it must be possible to clone humans in the near future. Then the debate we face will be about the cloning of people as beings that develop a culture, as opposed to *Homo sapiens*, family Hominidae, order Primates. It will have bearings on ethics. It will pose a question that is totally divorced from food production to enrich people's lives. It is unnatural, and it will not be accepted without a fight. It will require regulations that go beyond the realm of biology. However profitable it may be for some, it is conveniently inconsistent and selfish to regard part of a certain technology as being common to living organisms in general, while still placing human dignity above biology. Since people may use this technology for economic reasons, some argue that it is necessary to set regulations even at the experimental stage.

Before closing the topic of cloning, I would allude briefly to so-called man-made meat. In the hopes of mitigating the energy used in the process wherein animals eat vegetables to produce meat for human consumption, this technology produces a meatlike food directly from vegetables. It is now possible to taste beefsteak made directly from the soybeans. This plant-derived "meat" also has certain nutritional benefits. And it may be remembered that plant-based meat substitutes, nutritionally similar to animal protein, have been cooked as vegetarian food in Zen Buddhist temples for several centuries.

The transfer of life from one individual to another: a generational update
At what point is the life of an individual organism completed? Maybe there is no answer to this question. A new individual is born from procreation, where life is passed on from parents to children. This entire process in organisms is generally called reproduction. Maybe our role as living organisms is complete when we finish passing our life to the next generation. Eventually, an individual comes to the end of its lifespan and faces death. Some organisms, like trees, live for thousands of years in extreme cases, reproducing every year.

Does the change of generations bring new vitality? As a phenomenon, this is the case. Compared to an individual near the end of its life, an individual with more life remaining lives more vibrantly. The finite life expectancy of an individual may not be considered so important once it has fulfilled its role of passing life on to the next generation through reproduction. In that sense, is the death of an individual like casting off the husk of a life that created a new generation? To what extent is the death of an animal analogous to that of a plant?

Female humans procreate from their late teens to around their forties, which ensures there are individuals for the next generation. Male humans maintain their reproductive ability (i.e., their ability to produce sperm) for longer. Even so, the average human life expectancy is around 70 or even 80 in many developing countries. This must be because it takes time for the next generation to mature. Perhaps it takes even longer now for individuals of the next generation to mature socially, considering that life expectancy used to be around 50. There is a gap between the age of biological maturity, which allows for reproductive activities, and the age of social maturity, at which people are recognized socially as being fully grown; it is this which necessitated the extension of human lifespan. Furthermore, people take various artificial measures, including medical treatments, to avoid death. If the topic is broadened to this extent, it probably should be discussed in relation to every genre pertaining to human culture and civilization, not just in the realm of biology alone.

Learning from the dead

Humans communicate with each other by using language to exchange information. Human culture has entered a new phase in which the dead are able to influence the living even though they have passed away. Of course, a dead person cannot actually speak or convey any information to others; still, as explained in chapter 1, people receive a variety of information from the dead.

Wild animals learn how to live from their parents and the seniors in their population, usually by imitating these seniors' habits. A dead animal usually does not influence the behavior of younger animals. Modern human beings, however, usually learn a lot from people who are no longer living. Human culture comprises a gigantic amount of information accrued over human history, created by ourselves as well as by those who went before us. Our knowledge is based on information created by all human beings both present and past. We now have an educational system in which young people learn from their teachers how to live. Formal education is usually given in school in modern countries, though we learn a variety of things everywhere in daily life. We learn from the knowledge and behavior of our elders, both through language and actions. In addition, a valuable source of learning for people in the present is based on heritage preserved by those who have gone before.

Our behavior is influenced mostly by the education we receive from our parents and elders in our family, as well as elders in society. Being educated by social as well as family influences is an important part of growing and adapting to living in modern society. In this way, human beings act in their society even after they have passed away. The life-carrying materials, or individual bodies, are disassembled and scattered after their death, though their mental products are influencing individuals of our society, as if the dead people are still acting in our society. This does not apply to the life of organisms in general; it is particular to human culture. But I am alluding here to specific act of education shared by individuals after their death.

2. The Life of a Cell

The atoms and molecules that constitute a life-carrying body
What does it mean to say that an organism is alive?

The bodies of living organisms are made up of a huge number of atoms. Each organism has a specific proportion of elements, the building blocks of matter. Table 1 (page 22) shows the approximate weight ratio of elements contained in human body. The human body is 63 percent hydrogen and 25.5 percent oxygen, if the contents of atoms are compared; these figures suggest a large proportion of water molecules within the human body. Other elements that account for over 1 percent are carbon (9.5 percent) and nitrogen (1.4 percent). The next-largest figures are a mere 0.31 percent (calcium) and 0.22 (phosphorus). On table 1 are the ten most prevalent elements found in the human body; the other elements it contains, which are all present in very small amounts, are aluminum (Al), iron (Fe), manganese (Mn), bromine (F), vanadium (V), chromium (Cr), copper (Cu), boron (B), cobalt (Co), zinc (Zn), selenium (Se), molybdenum (Mo), tin (Sn), iodine (I), and others.

Although this ratio is generally stable, simply gathering elements in these proportions would not make a human body. Amassing atoms in a pile does not make them alive. This applies not just to living organisms; even a child knows that putting together the atoms composing a computer in the correct proportions does not make it a computer.

The atoms that make up the body in the proportions mentioned earlier do not exist separately as atoms. They all have a specific molecular structure. Water molecules are essential to the bodies of living things; the human body is two-thirds water. They are extremely important for organisms to attain the state of living. Water, in itself, is not alive. Water molecules, composed of two atoms of hydrogen and one atom of oxygen, are the same water molecules whether they exist in the human body or in the sea. They are not alive in themselves, though they do have unique properties. Life on Earth exists in water, a fundamental medium.

The story is slightly different, however, with organic matter containing carbon atoms, since organic matter can be created only by living things. Carbohydrates, which are generated by green plants via photosynthesis, become the source of organic matter. This does not mean that amassing sugar, for example, makes it a living thing, though it is a carbohydrate, just as mixing molecules that form a living organism in the correct proportions does not make them come alive.

Carbohydrates are quite significant as reserve substances and the source of energy. Nucleic acids and protein are the organic substances that play important roles more directly connected with life, for organisms to live. Such molecules, often called biopolymers, are regarded as the basic molecules of living structures and are essential for living tissues. Yet even those molecules that are vital for life can be preserved in the form of crystals. Once they are crystallized, they are no longer alive. Furthermore, viruses, composed mostly of nucleic acids, are not called living organisms because they are sometimes crystallized and turn into molecules, even though they demonstrate life activities under certain conditions, and are parasitic to living things.

Organic matter is created only by living things. If life were generated from inanimate objects, organic matter would be synthesized from inorganic substances under natural conditions where there is no living organism. That is what Stanley Miller demonstrated in his experiment in 1953: he used spark discharge as the source of energy on a mixture of gases—presumably of the same substances as the primordial atmosphere when organisms were born on Earth—to create amino acids and other organic matter. Model experiments like this proved that if life was born on Earth, the base materials were available.

Protein is synthesized within the body of a living organism, using nucleic acids as templates. One such nucleic acid, called deoxyribonucleic acid (DNA), is able to duplicate itself, using itself as the template. This self-replicating capacity is one of the essential features of living things.

It is possible to extract DNA from an organism and multiply it using a technique called polymerase chain reaction (PCR). Therefore, DNA, as a molecule, has a property that is extremely close to a life-form. Even so, if you remove a DNA molecule from a creature, it cannot function as a living thing.

Since DNA crystals are not considered alive, it may not be reasonable to call a few artificially cultured cells alive, either. Such cells can continue to live in the culture, but cannot do so in a natural condition. Crystallized viruses are not alive in themselves, but act alive under certain conditions, and are parasitic to the living organisms. Extracted and preserved DNA can retrieve the features of an organism via gene manipulation. From this viewpoint, it may be taking a break from the state of living, but has not stopped living altogether. It is all a matter of how to define "living," whether cultured cells are alive or not, and whether DNA preserved as crystals are alive or not. In biology, "living" is defined as the state of repetitious self-reproduction for a phylon.

Viruses

Most people are aware that the pathogen of COVID-19 is a kind of virus, commonly known as the novel coronavirus (see chapter 4). What are viruses, though? The word "virus" comes from Latin and refers to poison; it is generally known that viruses cause diseases in various organisms. Many different viruses have been identified and they actually work as pathogen of various diseases as cold, influenza, smallpox, the so-called Spanish flu, AIDS, SARS, MERS-CoV, and finally COVID-19.

The word "virus" was first recorded in English at the end of fourteenth century in the English translation of *De proprietatibus rerum* (On the Properties of Things) by Franciscan scholar Bartholomaeus Anglicus. The pathogen of the tobacco mosaic disease was observed in 1886 by A. E. Mayer (1843–1942); he considered it to be a minute bacteria, finding that it could not be observed by an optical microscope and that it passed through filter paper. D. I. Ivanovsky (1851–1931) observed in 1892 that this pathogen was smaller than bacteria, and would pass through even porcelain Chamberland filters. In 1898, M. W. Beijerinck (1851–1931) further developed the research on tobacco mosaic disease, naming the pathogen *Contagium vivum fluidum* (contagious living fluid), and recognized that this disease was transmitted by a pathogen other than bacteria. In 1898, F. A. J. Loeffler (1852–1915) worked on foot-and-mouth disease and found that the pathogen could pass through unglazed filters, and inferred that some other diseases like smallpox and measles were also caused by the same type of very small pathogens. In 1935, W. M. Stanley (1904–1971) succeeded in crystallizing the tobacco mosaic virus. These investigations established the science of viruses, or virology, which thus started with research into various pathogens, and then became generally known through the study of various diseases caused by viruses.

Some viruses are known to collaborate with the organisms that harbor them. In mammals, for example, a fetus is never attacked by its mother's body, thanks to the contribution of a retrovirus in the way of their co-evolution. This fact shows that viruses play a part in the evolution of organisms, and actually there are many viruses that co-exist with organisms on Earth.

A virus is a submicroscopic infectious agent that can only be replicated inside living cells. The current number of viruses is estimated as a figure of more than 30 digits; they are found everywhere in the biosphere and make up the principal element of the ecosystem. Viruses are parasitic to every kind of organisms and self-reproduce with nucleic acids (DNA and/ or RNA) as their genetic substances.

The systematic position of viruses has long been under discussion. They have been placed in an appendix of biological classification systems, rather than being cited as an actual component of the system. Viruses become viable when they infest other organisms, demonstrating self-reproducing phenomena like the duplication of DNA/RNA; but they can also be extracted and crystallized into DNA/RNA molecules; that is, a chemical substance. When a virus is in a crystalline state, it is not considered living matter. But it still behaves as a living organism, parasitic to other living organisms, borrowing metabolic activity from the cells of its host.

We do not know what the phylogenetic process was that enabled viruses to come into being, and it is difficult to determine where viruses should be placed in the phylogenetic relationship. One theory is that viruses were originally independent organisms, but they discarded unnecessary structures as they became highly adapted to the parasitic way of life, following an evolutionary path called simplification. As a result, they no longer have a cell structure, having been left only with DNA/RNA in their current state.

It is not impossible to surmise, however, that viruses are more biopolymers than organisms, as they are mostly composed of DNA/RNA and can turn into DNA/RNA crystals. This theory regards the DNA/RNA that make up viruses not as something that once evolved into living organisms, but as something that has been created independently of the existence of organisms, through the process of organic matter's complication becoming ever more complex; viruses, thus created, demonstrate DNA/RNA activities much as those of living organisms when they enter one. There is no evidence to back up this theory, but nothing to disprove it either. Therefore, viruses have sometimes been regarded as living organisms, and sometimes as inanimate matter, depending on the perspective.

In 2003, La Scola and his colleagues identified the so-called mimivirus, a giant virus in amoebae that was formerly considered to be Bradfordcoccus, a type of bacteria. This mimivirus is similar to a bacterium in appearance, but is actually a virus. It measures 0.75 μm in diameter and has a genome size of 1,200,000 pairs, and is unable to pass through an unglazed filter. It is easily observed through an ordinary optical microscope. Genome analysis of this mimivirus showed that it belongs to the group of nucleo-cyto-pamic large DNA viruses (NCLDV). Since then, various gigantic viruses have been observed and categorized as NCLDV.

Based on recent information, many biologists nowadays are inclined to consider placing viruses at the bottom of the biological classification system, recognizing a distinct clade of viruses independent from the clade of ordinary organisms (Eucaryotes and Bacteria) and that of Archaea. Now, we may recognize tentatively three super-domains in the spherophylon.

The diverse lives of cells

The current understanding is that molecules in themselves are not alive. Then what does it take at the minimum or basic level for organisms to be considered living? The answer is that the cell is the minimum unit of life, and all living matter has a cellular structure. Molecules are in living state only while they are elements of cells.

Unicellular organisms are those living in the form of a cell; a single cell carries out its life as an individual. The lives of multicellular organisms are carried out through the collaboration of many cells—in some cases, a huge number of them. Each component cell lives in its own way, and it

Fig. 3 Single-celled diversity

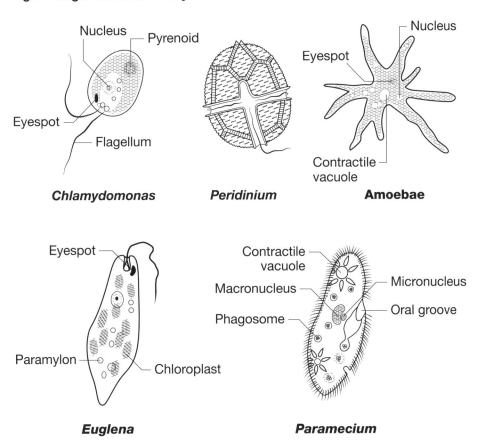

Chlamydomonas   *Peridinium*   *Amoebae*

Euglena   *Paramecium*

collaborates with its colleague cells, all of them having a close bond with each other.

Cells vary greatly in morphology and function, though their fundamental construction is more or less universal. There are many species of unicellular organisms, each of them different from one another. Individual multicellular organisms, generally speaking, are composed of a variety of cells; these usually collaborate closely with each other and show an integrated life enjoying a life of an individual. The component cells are distinct from one another, but they are not independent: they all work together to carry out life's functions perfectly. This is another phenomenon indicating that living is based on the integration of diverse existences.

Euglena and amoebae are often named as their examples of unicellular organisms. Surprisingly few people may have actually viewed single-celled organisms with their own eyes using a microscope, as they are invisible to the naked eye. Most people are aware, however, that they exist on Earth. The fact that there is a creature that lives in a single cell means that the cell itself is alive. All living things, originally, were single-celled. Currently, many of the organisms living on Earth are multicellular, but they are quite new in the history of life.

Even the newcomers, multicellular organisms, take the form of unicellular organisms somewhere in their lifecycle: as a reproductive cell (egg cell, spermatozoid, pollen, every kind of gamete) or zygote (fertilized egg). All living things do so, except those special ones that create a new generation via vegetative propagation.

With unicellular organisms, there is no distinction between an individual and a cell, as each individual consists of a single cell. On the other hand, multiple cells gather together to form a multicellular organism. Thus, an individual multicellular organism has different characteristics than a cell. Some individual multicellular organisms are composed of nearly the same type of cells, as seen in some filamentous organisms, though most multicellular organisms are composed of a variety of cells. In the case of humans, one individual consists of trillions of cells that differ with respect to their functions and structures. Cells have different purposes, and different cells with distinctive qualities, united together, make up an individual living being.

No matter how varied they are, the cells of living organisms have some universal qualities. For example, cells have an independent structure called a nucleus, in which DNA is arranged in a structure called a chromonema, wrapped up in a membrane (prokaryotic cells do not have a nucleus, and their DNA is distributed throughout the cell). The cells are filled with protoplasm, and the plasma switches between the sol and the gel states. Biomembranes are formed on the interface. Cells have various organelles, including mitochondria, a Golgi body, microsomes, chloroplasts (in the case of plants), and so on. Various molecules are gathered together to form a cell that is a structure with a certain order, that functions within the cell system, and that achieves self-reproduction, creating its unique history. The individual cells of a multicellular organism can be viewed as a live structural unit, alive in the same way that unicellular organisms are alive.

We should be clear about what parts cells need, at a minimum, to live. The simplest prokaryotic cells do not have a nucleus. Therefore, when a prokaryotic cell has DNA arranged in chromonema and a protoplasm including a ribosome, which enables the cell to function, it can be said to be alive.

However, a single cell of a living organism cannot live on its own. It is possible to remove human tissue and keep it alive in an artificial culture under certain conditions, but in nature, cells cannot simply pop out of the body and survive, except for germ cells.

An individual animal has a certain unity arising out of a certain process. If it is split in two, neither half can function as an independent individual (we exclude such phenomena as the regeneration of *Planaria* as an exception here). Even if the individual remains alive, the severed part cannot be called a living organism. It is only when a new generation is born that the number of individuals increases.

Some plants, however, can live independently as individuals when they are divided into several pieces, as can be seen in the case of bamboo groves and potato regeneration. With plants that conduct generation change without sexual reproduction—that is, through vegetative reproduction—the child's genes are generally identical to the parent's. The child is the parent's copy. They always clone themselves in a natural state, as it were.

Totipotency is recognized in plant cells; this means that a single cell is endowed with the same properties as the individual as a whole. A single cell has the same potential as an individual life-form, as the entire plant does. It is able to have a complete life.

Animals' somatic cells do not have totipotency. This does not mean that they have lost the attributes of the species; they have simply put them away for their daily activities. Cloning sheep proved that it is possible to awaken the totipotency in animals' somatic cells. In the case of a cloned sheep, one somatic cell generates the entire individual; that is, the cell lives the same life as that of one sheep. The life of this cell contains data parallel to that of a single individual, which it can express.

In this way, a single cell is able to live a complete life as an organism. Even the somatic cells of animals, which have lost totipotency, have the capacity to produce the next generation once it is activated. A single cell separated from a multicellular organism can live indefinitely, as long as it is cultured properly in a tube. All this clearly means that it is not that unreasonable to define the cell as the smallest living unit.

Cells multiply through a certain process: a mother cell splits into two daughter cells. Prokaryotes (bacteria) that do not have a definite nucleus structure in the cell become dented and split into two in the middle. This apparently simple division is called amitosis. In the cells of eukaryotes, which have a nucleus as a structure within them, DNA, consisting of filamentous threads within the nucleus called chromonemata, turns into a thick, short structure called a chromosome that has the double helix structure after the DNA are replicated. After a certain process that is common to eukaryotic cells, one mother cell produces two daughter cells identical to the original. The entire process of such cell division is called mitosis, or somatic cell division. In contrast, to produce gametes from a somatic cell that has two sets of DNA, a type of cell division called meiosis, or reduction division, takes place, which is common to eukaryotic cells. In meiosis, the partitioning of the cell is conducted twice after DNA is duplicated, or cell division, and resulting in four daughter cells with half the chromosomes of the mother cell.

Cells and multicellular individuals

The life of a unicellular organism is that of each cell carrying out its activities for living. In contrast, the life of a multicellular organism is conducted through the integrated collaboration of all the cells comprising an individual.

In the case of humans, it is estimated that each adult body consists of some 37 trillion cells; these cells are diverse in morphology and function. Our various human activities depend on a variety of cells: moving relies on muscle cells, protection from the environment relies on epidermal cells, supporting the body relies on cytoskeleton cells, digestion and absorption rely on gastrointestinal cells, reaction and thinking rely on nerve and brain cells, and so on. All 37 trillion cells are considered important elements of one's body without exception; we feel that even a single body cell of the 37 trillion should be carefully maintained.

It is our everyday attitude, however, to treat the cells of the body independently. When we have pain in one arm, for example, we consider the status of the epidermal and/or muscle cells of the wounded arm, not the gastrointestinal cells. Have you ever wondered whether one of the muscle cells in your chin is going to collaborate with a muscle cell in your foot? Usually, in your life, a muscle cell in your chin does not have any direct collaboration with one in your foot. Knowing this fact, we do not deny that both of these muscle cells are important elements of the body. All of us know quite well that we cannot maintain life without their perfect collaboration. We respect the integrated collaboration of all the 37 trillion cells that make up the body, recognizing that the activity of each cell is valuable in each independent activity.

It is evident that the lives of all multicellular organisms are based on the integrated collaboration of the cells that make up their independent individual bodies. The cells that comprise multicellular individuals are not unique, but they do display a diversity of form and function. The principle of life in multicellular organisms is based on the strong bonds between the diverse component cells. The cell is considered the minimum unit to conduct the phenomenon of life; in most multicellular organisms, component cells collaborate perfectly so that they are alive not only at the cellular level, but at the multicellular individual level.

3. The Ecosystem: Organisms Living in Collaboration

Creatures that one person has direct relationships with
Think about what you did today. How many different species of living things did you interact with?

Modern humans eat meals three times a day on average. Various animals, fungi, and plants are used as components of our meals. In Japanese cuisine, beyond the obvious ingredients like meat, fish and vegetables, bread and udon noodles are made of flour, and tofu is made of soybeans. Further, condiments such as miso paste, soy sauce, black pepper, and Japanese pepper also come from plants. The *shichimi* spice blend contains seven different components; all of them come from biological materials. Living matter contributes to desserts and sweets in various forms. It would be a challenge to count the number of different species of organisms we eat in a day. Nowadays, most are made of animals and plants particularly bred and cultivated for food, but these "artificial" organisms were originally wild.

The clothes we wear also come from living organisms. Wool is obtained from sheep, leather from various animals, and cotton and hemp come from plants. The raw materials (i.e., petroleum) of clothing made from synthetic fibers come from fossil organisms that were alive in prehistoric times.

With food and clothing accounted for, we should naturally consider housing, too. Wooden Japanese houses have particularly a deep relationship with plants; here, we must think not just of lumber, but also of wallpaper, the rice paper used for screens, and the straw mixed into mud plaster and used under tiles. Most furniture is made from plants and animals. There are even more species to count if we include plants in the garden or balconies, and pets. In addition, those little birds and insects that visit the garden must be friends that form an integral part of your life.

When we think about everyday life, we again find that various organisms are essential to us. Newspapers and books are made of paper manufactured from wood pulp, and ink also contains organisms or biogenic substances. When you switch on the light, the thermal power that generates the electricity uses fossil fuels. Without that electricity, we cannot watch TV or listen to the radio. We use paper, cloth, and many other biogenic materials for various games, too.

More directly, numerous kinds of organisms are living inside our bodies. Parasites such as roundworms and tapeworms may not be common nowadays, but everyone knows that we have living organisms that play a certain role inside the body, especially in the intestines. Colon bacilli are one example. E-Coli O-157 may be an unwanted guest, but if all the colon bacilli were erased from the human body, it would gravely endanger the host's life. We have quite a rich biota (flora) inside our bodies.

Everyone breathes; we breathe in oxygen and breathe out carbon dioxide. It is widely known even among primary school children that we owe this to plants, which use carbon dioxide to generate oxygen through photosynthesis, enabling all animals and fungi to continue to breathe in this way. Without plants, animals and fungi would not survive. The oxygen metabolism of plants themselves is also supported by their photosynthesis.

Even with these conspicuous examples, it is amazing just how many species of living organisms play a part in our daily life. Man may proudly call himself the Lord of Creation, but human life cannot be sustained even for a second without other creatures.

Creatures that have indirect relationships with people
It is not only humans that cannot live on their own as individuals. This goes for any single species; an individual organism does not live in

isolation from others. It is not the point that the animals and plants that we eat are cultivated animals and plants, bred by human technique. For all the wild creatures living in nature, existence is always dependent on relations with others.

The relationships of the organisms living on Earth are sometimes roughly divided into producers, consumers, and decomposers (figure 4). This classification is from the human perspective, and so rather cursory. Yet it gives us a starting point for a general understanding of the mutual relationships between the organisms living on Earth.

Producers are mainly green plants; they generate organic matter via photosynthesis, contributing to production by converting energy into organic matter. They of course need to live, and so they decompose organic matter to use the energy, consuming oxygen and releasing carbon dioxide for that purpose. In total, however, they release much more oxygen than

Fig. 4 Producers, consumers, and decomposers

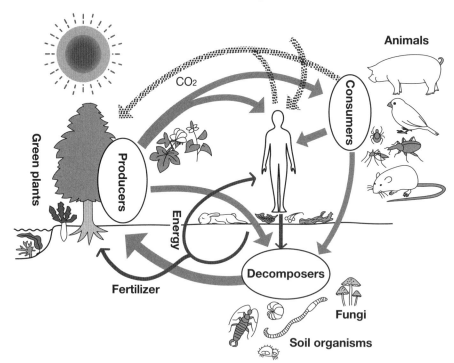

they consume, as they also accumulate organic matter. If we define producers as those that help increase the amount of stored energy, on balance, some bacteria that conduct chemical synthesis also fall into this category.

Consumers refers mainly to animals; they conduct activities using the energy that is generated when they decompose the organic matter they consume. Therefore, they consume oxygen and release carbon dioxide. As they cannot synthesize organic matter, they do not contribute to the binding of energy, but simply decompose organic matter. In that sense, they lead the same way of life as humans (a species of animal), who are naturally their competitors in energy use.

Decomposers comprise fungi and some soil organisms. They are not fundamentally different from consumers, but the emphasis is on decomposition and cleaning, rather than consumption, as they mainly consume the dead bodies of living organisms. Among animals, those that consume living organisms are pure consumers, but those that eat dead bodies to live, such as vultures, are decomposers, which live as cleaners of nature in a way. In the meantime, even some fungi are parasitic on living organisms; they do not do much in the way of decomposition, as they obtain energy directly from other living organisms. Therefore, it cannot be denied that the distinction between consumers and decomposers is subjective, as it is related to how organisms live.

Now, all the organisms living on Earth can be classified into these three categories, and they can lead a stable life on this planet when the three are in equilibrium.

The creatures that one person has direct dealings with today will each have some relationships with various other organisms. The organisms that people come into contact with also have inseparable relationships with various other organisms. Following those relationships, we realize that no creature living on this planet can live without having a relationship with others. Some may be deeply involved with others, while some may not have direct connections with others even once in their lives, never knowing that those organisms exist in this world. In fact, most relationships are the latter.

So far, approximately 1.8 million species have been identified and recognized on Earth, but it is surmised that a tremendous number of species, possibly over 100 million, inhabit the planet. All the individuals of those myriad species are living in one giant circle of relationships, even if they do not have direct dealings with each other. It is not just about those living around us. Creatures living on the opposite side of the planet may seem unrelated to our lives, but that only means they do not have direct connections with us; mutual relationships between organisms go around in a circle until it connects all of them. All the organisms on Earth are connected by a single thread.

The circle of life that forms the spherophylon

Cells are the most basic entity of life, but cells do not maintain their lives independently after a multicellular lifestyle has evolved. Apart from unicellular organisms, it cannot be claimed that a single cell is able to carry out its life independently.

In the meantime, no one believes that a single individual can live on its own, though an individual is a life-form that has a unified individuality, by definition. Yet not so many people have given serious thought to what complex and advanced connections we have as individual organisms with other living things.

It is known that no individual on Earth can live alone; every individual depends on the other individuals to sustain its life. It is true also for the species alive on Earth. No species on Earth, even though there are 100 millions of them, can live independently from any other species; every species collaborates with the others in various ways.

More than one species coexisting on Earth carry out life with other species; the life resulting from the collaboration of plural species is called an ecosystem. Many different ecosystems exist on Earth. Furthermore, all the extant species collaborate to make Earth into an ecosystem, developing their living area into a general biosphere.

Fig. 5 The range of the spherophylon

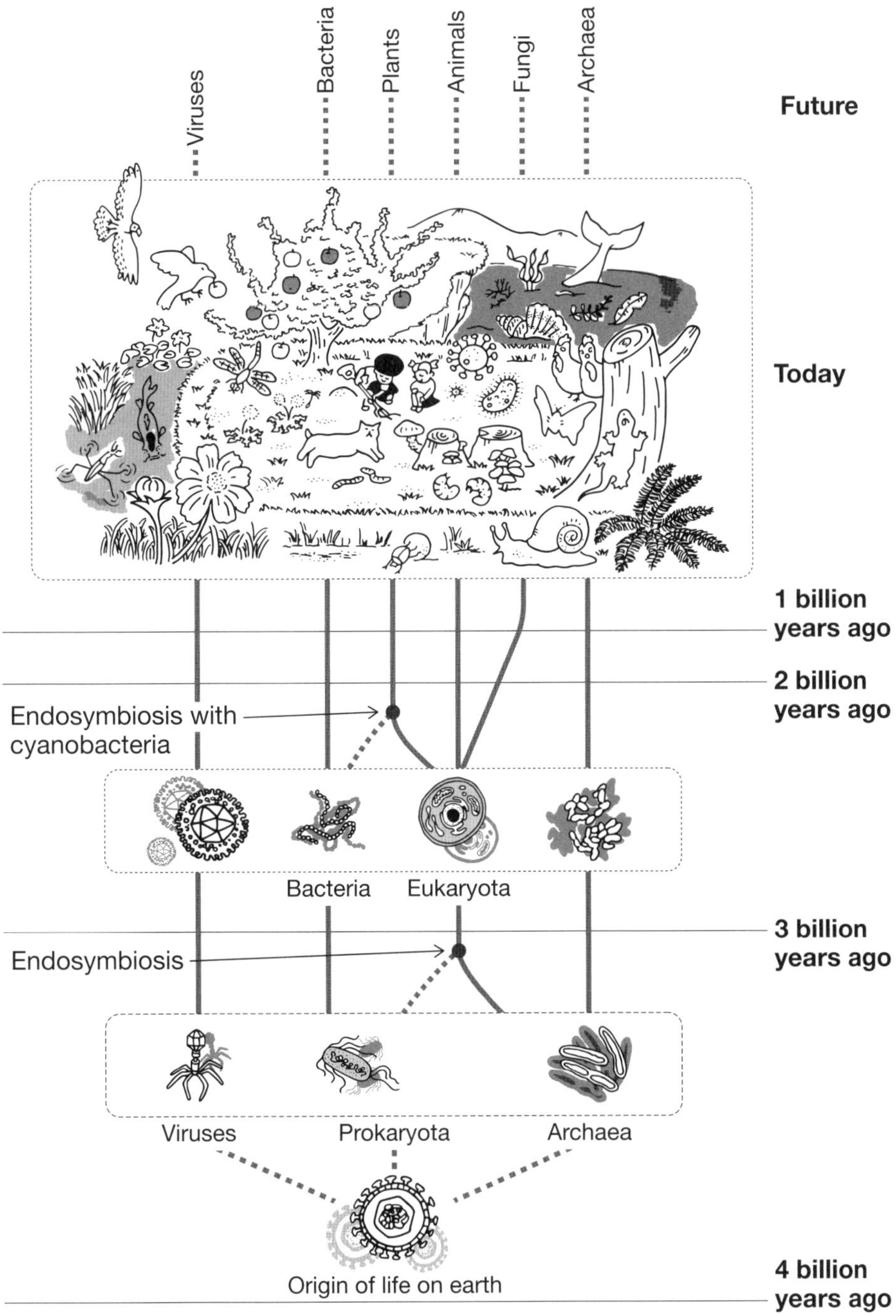

Viruses
Bacteria
Plants
Animals
Fungi
Archaea

Future

Today

1 billion years ago

2 billion years ago

Endosymbiosis with cyanobacteria

Bacteria   Eukaryota

3 billion years ago

Endosymbiosis

Viruses   Prokaryota   Archaea

Origin of life on earth

4 billion years ago

It should also be noted that no two ecosystems are the same, just as no two species are the same, and no two individuals are the same; every ecosystem on Earth is unique.

The minimum form of an ecosystem may be seen in symbiotic relationships, as discussed in the prologue, where two different species are completely interdependent. There are a number of typical examples, the life of lichens being an extreme example: every lichen species consists of a species of algae and a species of fungus, sometimes including symbiotic bacteria as well. It is somehow illogical to call an existing lichen species a biological species, for a species should be a fundamental unit, not one whose individuals consist of multiple individuals of different species. In the current biological classification, lichens are included in the list of fungi, based on the fungal species that are part of the symbiotic body.

A variety of ecosystems exist that can be defined as such both in structure and in function. Furthermore, every ecosystem has a direct or indirect relationship with other ecosystems; no single ecosystem is fully independent. The bonds between the ecosystems on Earth are variable and highly diverse.

What is the spherophylon?

As is repeatedly noted in this book, the spherophylon is by definition the only conglomerate living existence on Earth. It is a system comprising all the organisms on Earth, including its phylogenetic background; that is, the history of evolution during more than 30 billion years it has been taking place on Earth. The spherophylon has lived on Earth and developed its area throughout the entire biosphere; its timespan encompasses the complete evolutionary history of life on Earth.

Nowadays, it is widely accepted that the life of individual organisms is not complete, as can be seen in the phrase, "life forming the ecosystem." "Ecosystem" is a convenient term, as it can be used flexibly on a small or very large scale. When it is used to refer to a planet, it is equivalent to the biosphere. When we trace the world of living organisms from the level of molecules to those of cells, individuals, and ecosystems, it follows that the biosphere, which sits at the highest level, contains all the living organisms on Earth.

When we think about the spatial expanse of the biosphere, the term "Gaia" (Lovelock, 1988) comes to mind. This entity comprises all life-carrying bodies and their surrounding inorganic environment; that is, the Earth itself. The Gaia concept tends to regard the spherophylon and the inorganic environment as one. This book, however, regards life-carrying bodies that are under control of historical inevitability as having a distinctly different existence than that of inorganic objects.

The concept of the spherophylon which I propose is unique. "Biosphere" has a strong connotation, referring to an expanse that is currently composed of all the living organisms on Earth; it is a closed system, complete in the present time. Spherophylon should be defined more flexibly, not confined to the present but open to the past and the future, while still having a concrete presence as historical existence. In terms of the world of living organisms, the spherophylon is an ecosystem encompassing the entire planet just like the biosphere, with the basic understanding that the species and individuals forming the spherophylon maintain extremely close mutual relationships. These relationships are born in the past and continue on toward the future. That is, what is called the spherophylon here is a concept that is highly conscious of the fact that the spatial expanse that is meant by the term "biosphere" is backed by evolution, or the history of living organisms—that is, phylogeny. In other words, "spherophylon" refers to an entity that integrates the spatial expanse called the biosphere with the history of living organisms' evolution called phylogeny.

4. Individuals as Components of the Spherophylon

The current form of individuals and the spherophylon
If living organisms, which are so diversified that the number of species is sometimes estimated to be over 100 million, are all mutually connected in direct and/or indirect relationships on this planet, species and individual

living things can be regarded as one of the factors that form an integrated life on Earth as part of the spherophylon.

In the case of humans, one individual is made up of a huge number of cells (so huge that it would be expressed in a 14-digit figure). These cells take various forms, such as nerve cells that form the brain and the nervous system, muscle cells, epidermal cells in the skin, red blood cells, and others, but they are all endowed with the universality of being the cells of a living organisms. And all these trillions of the cells form a single human individual.

The relationship between an individual organism and the spherophylon is similar to that between a cell and a multicellular organism. Independent cells gather together under a certain system to form and live as a multicellular organism. In a similar manner, a huge number of independent individuals form the single spherophylon on Earth, having mutual impact under a certain order. Each individual life is complete in itself, and they exist as one factor of the circle of life that is united as the spherophylon.

Every individual organism living on Earth is part of the spherophylon, living a complete life; this is similar to the numerous cells that cooperate with each other to form a single multicellular organism. In that sense, we must not ignore the fact that our lives are one component of the spherophylon; just as our individual lives are not complete in themselves, life is not complete on the level of the spherophylon, either. We must not ignore the fact that we live as one component of the spherophylon.

Relationships between individuals vary in their intimacy; for example, individuals forming a family have very close relationships to each other. Small children cannot survive unless their parents earn money to buy food. When there is no parent, of course, people, or even wild animals, form a cooperative way of life to ensure the existence of the next generation. At the level of a village, some individuals may have such a distant relationship that they do not talk to each other even once in their lives. When it comes to countries, there are definitely more people one does not know than those one does, even within that country. The relationships between individuals become even more distant when it comes to the entire species of the human race. A person has a much closer relationship with the colon bacilli inhabiting their own body than with the humans who live on the opposite side of the planet. The organisms that you will consume as food today are much closer to you than unknown strangers living somewhere else on Earth. While they are all equal partners making up the spherophylon, you may have daily, frequent contact with some, but you may never in your life have direct contact with others.

The development of individuals and phylogeny

It may help to further understand the relationships between individuals and the spherophylon to compare their historical backgrounds; that is, their ontogenies and phylogenies. An individual organism starts its life as a fertilized egg. Through repeated cell cleavage and ontogenetic development, trillions of cells are created, all of which behave as a united individual (ontogenesis). Life created on Earth in a single form has been diversified through four billion years of history into extant species whose number is estimated at several tens of millions (phylogenesis). The colossal number of individuals living on Earth participates in forming the spherophylon through the species they belong to.

This explanation, however, reminds us of the so-called recapitulation theory, made famous by Ernst Haeckel (1834–1919, cf. next item) who posited that ontogeny is a shortened replay of phylogeny. Analogy, however, always contains the risk of wrongly explaining reality. Ontogeny is a process of building a life-form regulated by the genetic code contained in the fertilized egg and inherited from the parents; modifications and additional data are added, depending on the environment inside and outside the body, to form individuality. In the meantime, phylogeny, which has built the spherophylon, is not predetermined in its direction; it is a historical process, always containing the evolution of the species that are its components. It does not take further explanation to defend the fact that it is impossible to explain away everything by comparing the formation process of life-forms that are the vehicles of life and the living entity of the spherophylon.

It will take further, varied observations to determine how complete life is at the level of the spherophylon, however. An animal can live without a part of its body—a leg, for example. If a plant is split in half, both halves can regenerate the whole, independent individual. Even the spherophylon, as the entire unit of life on Earth, would not collapse if it lost one country—say, all the organisms living in Japan. If it were divided into the old and new worlds, for example, it might only differentiate into the spherophylon of the old world and that of the new world. Yet, there is this reality that life cannot be complete in individual beings; it forms the unit of the spherophylon to live. (The spherophylon might be able to regenerate if it were cut into one in the new and the other in the old world, though human beings could not survive if they were separated into two portions, as modern people are so closely interdependent on each other globally.)

Individuality is what integrates many cells into one individual. This unity is easy to understand in the case of animals, because one individual is born from one fertilized egg. Individuality is harder to recognize in the case of plants, as splitting one often directly leads to multiplication of individuals by vegetative propagation.

Numerous individuals and species together form the spherophylon on Earth, but they exist because life that occurred over three billion years ago differentiated into diverse species during the process of evolution. Many interrelated species and individuals that belong to those species are living on this planet, maintaining mutually inseparable relationships. It is the historical process called evolution that unites all these species and individuals within the spherophylon. It is quite difficult for extant science to recognize the spherophylon on Earth as a single entity, however, because its reality is largely hidden.

Haeckel's recapitulation theory and the spherophylon
Ernst Haeckel is known for proposing his recapitulation theory: ontogeny (the development of the individual) recapitulates phylogeny (the evolutionary background). Modern textbooks still use the similarity between development and evolution to explain evolution. Metazoan

animals—vertebrates in particular—take historically old forms to progress to more advanced forms after gastrula, the second embryonic stage, in the process of ontogeny. He therefore felt that the process of phylogeny, which took hundreds of millions of years, could be observed in the process of ontogeny, which takes only a few years at the most.

In the process of development, metazoans first create a pattern of cell formation, and develop that pattern to start growing. Unlike this, plants have cells that always possess the potential for differentiation in the tips of their stalks and roots, from which new tissues are created. The tissues that generate new ones are called apical meristems, and they function as an embryo throughout the plant's life. Therefore, a tree that is thousands of years of age is just like a baby—if it were an animal—at the tips of its stalks and roots. Hence, the recapitulation theory cannot be applied to the generation of the whole plant, but the theory can still be applied to plants if we limit the scope to the phenomena seen in the process of the formation of tissues and certain traits. Then, it becomes clear how insightful Haeckel's theory is. In fact, the developmental patterns between metazoa and vascular plants are different.

As mentioned before, the spherophylon on Earth can be compared to an adult individual. The first life-form that was generated on Earth corresponds to the fertilized egg of an individual animal. This first life-form (protobiont) eventually started diversification, but its early forms must have been quite similar to each other. Even in an individual animal, cleavage of a fertilized egg produces identical cells. (There are animals who have early cleavage with different forms of daughter cells.) Those primitive life-forms start to diversify, and differences between individuals become clearer. The cells that started with the fertilized egg start to have clear differences between them. As cleavage advances, the individual forms a morula, which changes into a blastula, and then into a gastrula after gastrulation. A simple cleavage drastically changes into a multicellular formation. Likewise, the spherophylon on Earth underwent a drastic change from the phase of prokaryotes to that of eukaryotes. Then, life differentiated into animals, plants, fungi, bacteria, and so on. After that, species, which are components of the spherophylon, accelerated diversification on the planet, with some venturing onto land. Individuals also undergo drastic changes to become adults.

This is not to say that the history of how the spherophylon evolved on Earth is reproduced in a shortened form in the ontogenesis of a certain species. Simply, just as a multicellular organism gradually takes-on a unified form as an individual, so did the spherophylon become complete as an aggregate of the various organisms living on Earth. We would then ask: Is the form of our spherophylon comparable to an adult that is in the final phase of developing as an individual? We do not have enough information to answer this question. To discuss the entity of the spherophylon on this planet, we need to analyze and understand what it is more accurately and more meticulously.

Chapter 4

Science, Nature, and Humanity

1. What Science Has Given Us

What we do not know

Natural science has made progress by leaps and bounds. Such feats of science further prompted the development of advanced technology. Over time, awed by science and technology, people became overly confident in their ability. It was almost as if people were foraying into areas that had until only recently been said to be the realm of gods. It seemed humanity had a rosy future, having diverse future dreams. You would almost think we could conquer the universe—not just Earth—securing eternal prosperity, if humankind, having thus prospered, continued to establish advanced technology further.

Yet why are we seeing environmental issues, starting with pollution problems, become global issues? Why are problems such as the loss of biodiversity and global warming perceived as environmental issues for humanity? Why are we warned that the twenty-first century will be one of starvation for human beings, even as we have all these fantastic dreams? Why can we not resolve the hazards that drive us ever closer to ruination, even with science and technology that are so far advanced?

Science has made amazing progress every day, shedding light on the unknown, little by little. Questions about historical processes like evolution were said, when we were university students half a century ago, to be nearly impossible to prove empirically, throwing some people into agnosticism, making them doubt that they would be ever solved with a scientific approach. Great headway is now being made in such areas based on scientific demonstrations, thanks to subsequent progress in the research of microfossils and developments in molecular phylogeny.

For those engaged in scientific research, however, newly discovered facts are doors to further impenetrable questions. In other words, scientific discoveries do not tell us everything about a certain thing; uncovering some facts only reveals what we do not understand. If so, does it not follow that the fact of science's stellar progress and infinite discoveries suggests just how many unsolved questions it has posed to us? What does it mean that, even though science has made such progress, there is no single field that has declared that there are absolutely no more mysteries to be solved?

Natural science is a field that unravels truths in nature. Science has greatly contributed to revealing universal principles found in natural phenomena. It has indeed discovered laws and principles in typical, fundamental, and ideal conditions, but various phenomena in nature do not occur in such a simplified state. They emerge when diverse laws and principles converge. It is expected that the reality of various phenomena in nature will be uncovered by science in the coming days, based on the discovery of new laws and principles. We should clearly realize that we still know very little about the natural phenomena that manifest in various forms.

Realize how little we know

Scientists proudly talk about discovered facts. Textbooks list things that have been brought to light quite persuasively. So-called experts in special fields explain so many things based on their scientific knowledge in their area, as if there is nothing they do not know. If they confess they do not know something, they may be accused of having insufficient knowledge in their specific field. Generalists decry those earnest researchers who apologize for failing to explain "unknown facts," saying they cannot be called "experts" in an era when science has uncovered so much. Science has, actually, uncovered just how much is unknown about this world.

Experts should be defined as those who know better than anyone else how ignorant we remain.

When we think about our immediate concerns about the environment and resources, what we can do is frighteningly little, as we look around us. Still, we deal with present issues by the convenient problem-solving method of shelving, by making use of overconfidence and mistaken trust in science and technology.

I am not trying here to characterize the knowledge and insight gained by science as being incomplete. Science has made great progress in the past 50 years alone, and I pride myself in thinking that I have personally contributed to making that progress, however small my contribution may be. What I want to stress here, however, is that science still does not know everything, and that there is so much it cannot do because it is incomplete. This is such an obvious fact, but it is so important that we should not do anything unless we understand it correctly, since most of the problems we face today are things that we need to be careful with purely because we do not understand them. If we only needed to deal with known issues, we would simply predict the future, deal with whatever we can manage, and bear whatever we cannot, realizing that these issues cannot be solved. With unknown problems, however, we cannot predict what will happen. We should therefore take a sufficiently large margin for the danger zone, lest we face serious issues. Yet we are taking measures now against what is assumed to be hazardous based on the minimum estimates of the hazard level. It is only natural that the hazard will become reality. Even when an accident happens, even when ~~we~~ there are many casualties, we repeat the excuse that it could not have been avoided. Those lost lives will never come back to life. We may be able to at least express our regret for those accidents that are made public, but no one takes responsibility for incidents that insidiously undermine people's physical and mental health. We even avoid facing the fact that they are hurting us.

We need to remember the old days, and humbly think about how little we know about nature, and about the planet. Arrogance comes back to haunt those who are steeped in it. We need to take special care that our code of conduct is not governed by overconfidence due to ignorance.

Make people understand that they do not understand

Natural phenomena contain an infinite number of inexplicable mysteries that we have not deciphered. People explain things that they understand using accurate expressions, but make hypotheses for things that they do not understand, as they cannot be explained empirically. Quite often, in fact, things are explained away cleverly by inference alone based on those hypotheses. The public accepts both proven explanations and inferred explanations as facts. If you object that certain things are not verified, people will stubbornly refer to some authority in the field who taught them otherwise, suggesting that anyone who insists that we have yet to understand the matter is in fact ignorant.

Things that we do not understand are mysterious; they trigger our curiosity. Driven by curiosity, we try to understand what we do not. And this is the first step in science. To conduct research, we need to make hypotheses on unverified phenomena based on knowledge already acquired, and when these hypotheses are proved scientifically, we can say we understand those phenomena. Yet there are so many cases where we claim to understand unknown phenomena by explaining them away based on known facts. This is merely explanation—not scientific discovery, which can only be complete when the hypotheses are proven.

Some hypotheses are treated as if they are the final answers. Some old assumptions are sometimes proven correct after many years, and are lauded for their insight. This, however, is like guessing a puzzle correctly. If an assumption is correct, a hypothesis can be made logically, which is easy to verify. Scientifically excellent assumptions bring about progress in science. Yet, assumptions are only that: assumptions. And hypotheses are only hypotheses. It is not so important whether they turn out to be correct or not. Verifying hypotheses to prove them is the way to get to the bottom of natural phenomena. Only correct hypotheses can be proven to be true, however. Therefore, making correct hypotheses is an important skill for scientists.

Interesting hypotheses sometimes bring about paradigm shifts, and are significant in themselves. It is not unheard of, however, that proven facts are ignored in order to make interesting stories. (If such a hypothesis is made use of for political ends, it may lead to tragedy. We must be aware that there are recent examples of this; it is not limited to the ancient past.) Interesting stories are often perceived as being constructed by specialists. The human intellect, however, must not be built upon fiction. We must build schools of thought by clearly distinguishing what is proven—what is known fact—from what is just explained without having been proven.

There is so much that we do not understand about natural phenomena, which hold a wealth of unknown mysteries. Instead of being content to explain them away, we should solve them scientifically, one by one, to uncover the hidden facts, and consider them deeply to determine how we should live. For that, it is vital that scientists communicate facts correctly to the public and make the intellectual joy of solving an enigma something more familiar to the general public, instead of just making stories interesting. Fundamental science will prosper steadily only if the general public wishes it to happen.

How far can something be proven?

Scientists consider things that are verified to be things that are understood. The public, however, makes use of this or not, at its will. If something cannot be proven to be safe, we may choose to turn a blind eye, and if it is not demonstrably unsafe, we-will fully decide we need not worry, as no one knows whether it is safe or not. Even when there is some risk, if the risk is not so high, we may suppress the voice of warning for the sake of immediate commercial advancement, even though it is not proven to be without risk.

It is only natural that people take risks in their lives, but they should do so while knowing the risk. If there is any slight risk, it should not be hidden. If people are aware of the risk and make their own choice to take that risk for the sake of a better life, if an accident happens, no one will make excuses later that there actually was a risk or that the action was beyond our current technology. We only need to face the fact that the risk, which was considered to be slim, unfortunately became reality, and take corrective to prevent a similar incident from occurring.

If we took action only when we knew absolutely everything empirically, modern life would not be possible. Though we do not understand many things, we take them on, trusting the gut feelings that we have acquired from experience. This is probably how organisms are supposed to live in the first place. Something went wrong when people, learning a little about many things, started to become self-assured in their knowledge. It is often the case that people hide the fact that they do not know something by making plausible explanations about it. Treating things that we do not understand as if we do understand them causes various distortions. We can no longer distinguish things we know from things that are explained as if we know them.

Suggestions from so-called experts are highly valued by the media, and most people easily follow their suggestions. The knowledge offered by these experts is said to have been elucidated by modern science, and it is still far from encompassing everything about nature. We should not decide how to face various problems by simply following these suggestions without question. The opinions of experts arise from their judgement based on the information they have at hand. For our own behavioral guidelines, we should always think for ourselves based on the facts elucidated by science and informed by the experts in the specific field concerned; our action must be based on our own judgement, for which we are responsible.

2. What Science Is Capable of Now

Earthquake prediction: a case study of scientific precognition
It seems that technology is making infinite progress before our eyes. We often even fall prey to the mistaken belief that nothing is out of our reach. Nonetheless, we often witness situations that we cannot control. Pollution

issues accompanying technological advances are still not a thing of the past. Can it be said that we are taking sure and sufficient measures against global warming? Enormous anxiety is looming over the issue of the resources that will sustain humankind in the present century, and there is no end to the risks posed by natural disasters.

Quake-ridden Japan naturally started full-scale research on earthquake prediction long ago. Still, in 2011 we were not able to predict a major earthquake in East Japan, which did not have a prediction system set up; even in central Japan, where prediction research is conducted on a large scale, it is not guaranteed that it is possible to predict earthquakes sufficiently in advance.

This is only natural, as we do not understand nature well enough yet. Our current knowledge of the geoscience of earthquakes is as yet insufficient, as is the case in every other field of science. It is not possible to predict accurately, without fail, when and where earthquakes will occur, and what their magnitude will be, well in advance, when we have inadequate information. Some may therefore think that injecting a massive amount of funding into earthquake prediction research is a fraud. This is not so, however. Although science has not yet discovered how to make accurate predictions at a certain time before an earthquake occurs, it is not the case that our current science possesses no knowledge regarding earthquakes whatsoever. If there is something that we know with certainty, we can pursue the possibility of earthquake prediction by building on that knowledge. Mind you, it is only the pursuit of possibility. If it were possible to predict the occurrence of an earthquake even immediately before it happened, there would be a large possibility of partially avoiding what could be a serious disaster. If there is even a slight chance of accomplishing this, is it not obviously the duty of scientists to do so? I am not a specialist in the field of earthquake prediction, but most people agree on this if we discuss scientific knowledge and its benefits.

Information that biology has uncovered about biodiversity, even about recognition of species, may be about 10 percent—or even less than 1 percent—of all there is to know. What we know about species recognition is akin to knowing two or three people in the megalopolis of Tokyo, whose population is over 10 million people. Furthermore, we need to know what is useful in order to develop useful resources. For that purpose, the complete DNA base sequences of some organisms have been identified, but we are still far from discovering necessary facts with respect to recognizing wildlife in general as a potential gene resource to secure hope for the future. So it is not in anyone's power to come up with the correct answers to questions about the realities of biodiversity at present and in the future, when we know so little about it. However, it is not impossible even now, based on that scarce information, to make proposals about how to maintain biodiversity in the future environment of the planet. In fact, various proposals have been made, and not a few of them have been acted upon properly. Furthermore, we are sometimes able to issue a strong warning about the danger of not taking urgent action. Those who are in possession of scientific facts must to do so for the sake of the planet's future safety.

The crisis of biodiversity will not manifest itself immediately, nor will it bring catastrophic damage detrimental to the survival of human beings today; unfortunately, it is extremely difficult to gain a general understanding of the gravity of the matter. In contrast, the public loudly demands solutions for earthquake prediction, as we can directly witness the large-scale disasters caused by earthquakes. For issues for which the public insists on a solution, countermeasures must be taken at minimum. For issues about which general understanding is not yet gained, those who predict the danger also have the duty of speaking out to enlighten the public, if they foresee a definite risk. It is also a choice to decide on pursuing only our present prosperity, while being fully aware of the danger, saying that we do not have the luxury of caring about our descendants.

The need to further enhance earthquake prediction research was identified lately; it was also acknowledged that basic research on earthquakes should be urgently supported. If we have been remiss in either field, we need to take a serious look at our actions now. The same can be said about biodiversity: we need to take action on what needs to be done now as public undertaking, based on our current knowledge. At the same time, it is absolutely necessary—not just for scientific development but also for the foundation of humankind's future—to continue to promote research on basic knowledge, which is nowhere near where it should be.

Global warming and biodiversity

Accurately predicting how global warming will progress is a difficult task. The fact cannot be denied that it is triggered by increases in carbon emissions. It is certain that how it will progress, or how it should be allowed to progress, is mostly up to people's discretion. There have been serious natural disasters everywhere on Earth in recent years, and it is often explained that they have been induced by global warming. It may be so, though we have no scientific evidence to prove it. Nothing definite about the impact of global warming on the planet's environment is in evidence, although the information available strongly suggests it. It can be safely said that global warming will accelerate and will most certainly impact biodiversity if it continues to deteriorate, but no one has solid ground for asserting how crucial the impact will be. Science has not advanced sufficiently to allow us to make a complete prediction.

It is not yet possible to empirically prove the effects of global warming on biodiversity. Highly aware of the importance of this issue, we compiled a list of the problems that Japanese researchers studying biodiversity faced, and wrote a book attempting to divine what we could foresee from them (Domoto and Iwatsuki, 1997, 2000). What no one can deny is that rapid global warming will have a tremendous impact on the planet's spherophylon. There is no objective way to prove exactly how tremendous it will be. It cannot be said that the phenomenon currently predicted will be the death of this spherophylon, for example, but there is no positive proof that it will not bring about disastrous consequences. People often choose to take out insurance of some kind if there is some risk of danger. Those who do not like to feel daunted by a threat, under the influence of immediate gains and losses, may take a devil-may-care stance, however, and decide to go as far as they can without having any insurance.

Though we know that our actions will definitely bring about global warming, we find it hard to reduce our carbon emissions to prevent it. The human race might face mass fatalities in the near future; still, it is said to be impossible to prevent that from happening. The Paris Agreement was approved in 2015 at COP 21 for Climate Change, and most signatory countries agreed to reduce their carbon dioxide emissions. Still, there are barriers to surmount, and promotion of this project faces various difficulties. Is this because of the limited extent of our technology? I do not think so. It is not that our technology has not reached the level of averting imminent disaster. It is only that people have decided that it is not worth investing in technological development at the cost of their fortunes, willfully presuming that the lives of theirs and their close friends and families will not be affected, though there is no guarantee that this will be the case. If they know that their own lives really are at stake, people will take whatever preventive measures are necessary.

Science cannot predict precisely how much the planet will warm over the next 100 years. Maybe it is not for science to predict a future that is at the mercy of people's actions. It is possible to come up with some possible figures, however. There are some highly probable events that can be predicted. If something might bring on disaster, should we not remove the cause with as much certainty as possible? After all, that is how people have sustained and fostered civilizations. That is what we should do now. Yet they say it is difficult to reduce carbon dioxide emissions. Is it really difficult? As I said earlier, the difficulty does not lie in technological deficiency. It is a matter of motivation. It was decided that it would be fine not to make that effort. Who made that decision? And those who did, how are they going to take responsibility for the next generation of the human race, not just for themselves? Maybe "responsibility for the next generation" is a thought that does not come across the minds of those caught up in the wealth they have today. I do wish they would stop making it look as if their decision were the consensus of the entire world. They should at least admit openly that they are shirking their responsibility for the future in order to secure their own immediate gains.

When we take action of some kind, we make every possible prediction about various possible consequences, and think of steps to take against potential outcomes in advance. If it is not possible to make accurate predictions, we normally take measures based on the most conservative estimate in order to have plenty of margin for safety. Even then, unforeseen accidents do occur from time to time. We have to be prepared for that eventuality, and have some security accordingly. This is how the human race has successfully built civilizations. When an entrepreneur starts a business, they take responsibility for it. Unlike individual businesses, however, no one assumes responsibility for the consequences of human acts on a global scale. We defiantly think, "Why should I/my country alone be responsible?" Why do we take such devil-may-care attitude? This responsibility should be borne equally by all of us on planet Earth. Should we go and risk ruination of our planet for the sake of petty benefits to ourselves, to our companies, or to our nations? It must be clear to you readers, who have read this book so far, what price such a mindset forces the life of the spherophylon on this planet to pay.

Changes in organisms brought on by global warming
We need to be prepared to handle various situations, which we are not quite sure will happen due to scarcity of information, in case they do occur. If our knowledge is deficient, we must make efforts to uncover more facts. That is scientific curiosity. Learning it better to take possibly securer steps—this is the essential attitude for human beings to protect the eternal life of the spherophylon on Earth.

In order to have a better idea of what global warming will cause to the spherophylon, we need to have better knowledge. This means much more basic data. Here I will list some examples of plant distribution that are distinct to the Japanese archipelago.

Take *Trachycarpus fortune* (Hook.) H. Wendi, or windmill palm, as a typical example. This is a species of palm trees that is grown in various parts of south and central Japan, presumably native to the southern part of Kyushu. Now, this palm plant has been springing up in groves everywhere, even in eastern Japan, in recent years. Plants do not spring up easily outside their natural habitat, though windmill palm trees are cultivated in many places. Yet they have been emerging like weeds, even in the botanical garden of the University of Tokyo, which is right in the middle of the city, causing havoc to vegetation control for some time now. I have witnessed seedlings growing spontaneously in forests and bamboo groves in the village near my house in Yokohama. Those seedlings sprouted in areas protected by forests and bamboo groves back then. Nowadays, they are even more vigorous; they emerge in exposed, windswept places, even in a small garden like mine. When they started springing up in the university's botanical garden, it was possible that it was due to the effect of urbanization. We can no longer comfortably conclude that that is the reason, now that they grow wild in the village near my house, or further in the mountain forests in Okutama in western Tokyo.

Another example to be taken up is the case of the maidenhair fern, *Adiantum capillus-veneris* L. This species was formerly known only south of southern Kyushu. It was around 1960 when this species was found on Mount Rokko near Kobe. At that time, it was simply explained as an escape from the Rokko Mountain Botanical Garden, and was extinct in the succeeding winter season. This species is now commonly observed on stone walls around Akasaka, center of Tokyo, and even along the gutters near my house in Yokohama (color plate). They grow by themselves and live beyond the winter season; now they are recognized as native there.

The Chinese ladder brake, *Pteris vittata* L., also grows freely throughout the city, though the southern limit of its natural habitat used to be southern Kyushu (color plate). I am not sure if this has come from a greenhouse nearby or if it has moved northward from its native site by dispersing its spores.

Similar phenomena that must be caused by the influence of global warming, though not 100 percent proven scientifically, have been observed in different organisms in various locations in recent years. We cannot entirely conclude that individual cases are the consequences of global warming, but by amassing cases that can be called objective evidence, we can identify changes in biological distribution caused by global warming. Such evidence tells us that the movement of biodiversity has been partially disturbed at times, leading us to realize that we are seeing the emergence of a significant impact on the equilibrium of biodiversity. Some say that what is happening now can be sufficiently surmised without accumulating a large amount of side evidence, but we need to clearly establish facts even if we must work hard to do so, if we are to convince those who are skeptical.

COVID-19 and the life of the spherophylon

The recent COVID-19 pandemic is a difficult issue to overcome even around the concept of spherophylon. The life of the spherophylon has been seriously damaged by the COVID-19 pandemic, and the future of the spherophylon will be influenced by it to some extent. The unusual activities of people during the pandemic have influenced both domestic and wild organisms in various ways, thus causing harm to the life of the spherophylon. We should try to improve the life of the spherophylon whether COVID-19 becomes more active or less in days to come.

COVID-19, or coronavirus disease 2019, is the name of the disease that launched the pandemic in 2019. The so-called COVID-19 virus is a virus (cf. chapter 3-2) identified as SARS-CoV-2; this pathogen of infection attacked humans. When SARS-CoV-2 is parasitic to a human body, it is so active that the host human suffers from high fevers and lung damage, often resulting in the death of the host. When the virus is active in the human body, it rapidly multiplies (reproduces), templating itself, and its activity in fact strongly influences the life of the spherophylon.

Generally speaking, human infection is disease caused by various microorganisms called pathogens. I myself was infected by scrub typhus, carried by the red tick, in Laos in 1995, as well as by amoebiasis carried by *Entamoeba histolytica* in Chile in 2002. These infections, transmitted by small animals, are not rare in the countries concerned, though they are infrequent, never rising to the level of a pandemic. An example of an infection by a particular virus that can cause a pandemic is influenza. We do not know when the COVID-19 pandemic will be controlled, nor whether any other virus will bring the next pandemic to human society. (We know that smallpox has been completely extinct on Earth since 1980, though this is a rather rare case.) Controlling COVID-19 infection, as well as establishing treatment for it, is an urgent task that we face, and prevention of any future viruses is a duty that modern humans must always take care of.

COVID-19 influences *Homo sapiens*, though it probably originated in animals other than humans. We also encounter a variety of pandemic infections in domestic animals: beef anthrax from oxen and cows, classic swine fever from pigs (suspected to be carried by wild pigs), bird flu from chickens (often carried by wild birds), and so on; these cause livestock farmers serious harm. Furthermore, these examples all influence the present life of the spherophylon. We should take responsibility for controlling pandemics of such diseases for the sake of humans as well as the animals concerned to sustain the safe and healthy life of the spherophylon.

Recently it has been said that sustaining "one health" is important at the moment. This term implies that precautions for animal diseases should be considered in the same category as medical care for humans. The wisdom of the one health concept goes without saying if we consider the health of the spherophylon.

3. Research on Biodiversity

Biodiversity and the spherophylon
Earth's spherophylon has a single life. I put it like this because the spherophylon has established a unique structure with functions that diversified into tens of millions of species in the history of evolution spanning more than three billion years. It is indeed a gargantuan entity that transcends time and space. Therefore, uncovering the truth of the spherophylon on Earth means shedding light on its historical background, gaining full knowledge of the global expanse at the same time, and finally fathoming the principles of the entity of life that transcends time and space.

In the meantime, research on biodiversity is based on learning the characteristic features of all organisms growing on Earth and identifying their historical background. That is to say, understanding the life that forms a single phylon on Earth leads to the unraveling of biodiversity.

Biodiversity research was formerly called taxonomy. This field of science was often considered to be simply enumerating the variety of organisms, and was excluded from the area of pure science research analyzing principles of nature. Some questioned the validity of taxonomy as scientific study until very recently. Classifying living things, however, has consistently been connected with understanding what it means for organisms to live; for that reason, taxonomy tried all the more to identify how various organisms existed, how they were formed historically, and with what phylogenetic relationship. Some taxonomists did not understand this very well, or refused to try. The reality is that in any field of science, we have good scientists and those who are not necessarily good. Only those who do not understand the source of the problem will take up the rhetoric of inferior proponents to criticize the study itself.

It is not only due to the change of the term from taxonomy to biodiversity research that progress in the research is now eagerly awaited. It is because knowledge acquired in diligent research since the old days of taxonomy is now being analyzed in wider areas. There is a huge need for more knowledge regarding this planet's spherophylon in various fields. Beneath the act of learning lies the anticipation of mastering the object.

Biology and biodiversity research
Scientific development in Japan was left to researchers' individual efforts, with hardly any support from the government or society, until the mid-twentieth century, when I started my scientific career. Consequently, it was the social norm for good scientists to endure poverty, living like social failures, which would be extolled as the touching story of a true scientist. As the sentiment went, it was their choice to do scientific research, so they were welcome to do it as they please. Incidentally, this attitude was also applied to artists, who also chose to create art that no one asked for. It

further followed that researchers should make use of basic data necessary for the development of technology that was available from somewhere else. Since scientific research is conducted globally, there was no need to inject massive funds into developing science on their own. While that was the public view, even for scientists, there was a fine line between scientific research and the hobby of rich men. Unless you were well-off, it was not possible to be engaged in scientific research back then. Biodiversity research, especially, was given the nickname of "lordly biology."

Things couldn't remain in this state forever. In the latter half of the twentieth century, competent people took active roles in contributing to science, while frameworks were built—though gradually—where the government and society took charge in pushing scientific research forward. It was around that time that biological sciences made great progress under the banner of DNA, reaching a par with, and then becoming even more advanced than, physics and chemistry. Even so, biodiversity research was not able to completely shake off its somewhat avocational nature. Beguiled by individual facts, the enthusiasts among the researchers pursued what they loved most. They tended to get hung up on individual facts, delving deep into them, without giving a thought to seeking universality in the phenomena of life. Many researchers engaged in biodiversity were losing sight of what science is, instead getting caught up in the fascinating phenomena they were exploring. Placing value on engaging individual facts and stubbornly insisting on their own viewpoints—though that was nothing but bluffing—they eventually caused their own undoing. It cannot be said that there is no shadow cast over the future of biodiversity research, when it should be pushed forward, without taking a fresh look at this properly.

Molecular biologist Jacques Lucien Monod (1910–1976) once said something to the effect that a fact ascertained in colon bacilli is a universal fact that applies to all living things. Jumping to the wrong conclusion, some people mistakenly concluded that once they unraveled the life of colon bacilli, they would solve all the mysteries of what it means to be alive. They lost their universal perspective on this matter. Those who derided them, pointing out that learning everything about colon bacilli did not enable them to understand the movement of an elephant's trunk, were no better than those people they laughed at for lacking universal perspectives of their own. Whether it is colon bacilli or an elephant's trunk, individual facts do not allow us to understand what it means to live. An elephant has a trunk. This fact cannot be ignored. If it had no trunk, though, would that take anything away from the fact that organisms are alive? It is true that elephants are living on Earth, and it is not possible to conceive of the spherophylon without them. We then need to ask what elephants' trunks mean for the life of the spherophylon on this planet. Only when the movement of elephants' trunks is understood—the trunks being regarded as one of the traits that make up the spherophylon—can the discovery be one step in a science that embraces the universality that helps us solve the mystery of life.

Nowadays, many people have come to understand how indispensable biodiversity is to human life. There is a global consensus on the fact that sustainable use of the components of biodiversity is essential for human survival on Earth, and the Convention on Biological Diversity was adopted at the UN Conference on Environment and Development, also known as the Earth Summit, in 1992.

What are the immediate issues for biodiversity study? In the 1990s, we proposed to establish an institute named BoSSCo that would aim to do the following: First, it would encourage basic research on biodiversity on a global scale to discover unknown information about what sorts of organisms live in what parts of the world. Second, it would promote analytical research on the biological challenges of biodiversity based on basic data already acquired. Third, it would conduct social education using exhibitions and establish freely accessible informational systems so that the general public could avail themselves of existing knowledge on biodiversity. It takes a massive research organization to handle all these tasks. The UK's Royal Botanic Garden, Kew, has the total of 500 full-time employees, including researchers and maintenance staff; BoSSCo, if possible, should be even bigger.

Japan has a longstanding organization called the Geographical Survey Institute (GSI), which meticulously conducts basic research on geography. It is widely acknowledged that it is an indispensable organization, and in fact, the GSI contributes to society in various ways. For the future of humankind, it is necessary to prepare basic data on biodiversity as meticulously accurate as that of the GSI. In fact, biodiversity takes a far greater amount of data when it comes to sheer volume of information, as explained in chapter 4.2. Yet we are unable to create an organization to collect that data. Why is this?

As it is often said, war triggers rapid progress in technology, and also in the science underlying that technology, as we have seen in history. War is about killing each other for the sake of national survival. People would go to any length, pay any price, to win a war. The entire nation avidly pursues the development of technology and science that will contribute to victory. This may not be always the case, but it is not so difficult to establish a research institute related to war efforts during a certain period. For example, because knowledge of the relevant terrain is vital to formulating war strategies, nations do not mind investing in the collection of topographical data. The predecessor of the GSI belonged to the Army General Staff Headquarters during the war, so it must have encountered no resistance in building a research institute of this scale. (Mind you, this is not intended as a criticism of the GSI—in fact, we would like such information to become even more refined and accurate.)

What I want to emphasize here is that there has been no research institute built for something far removed from war like biodiversity during times of war and other contingencies. People do not understand the urgent need for a biodiversity research institute, even though biodiversity is deeply entwined with human survival; they question the sudden need for such investment during this peaceful time. Humanity actually faces a situation far more terrifying than war, but maybe people caught up in everyday life do not understand that.

BoSSCo should draw attention as an area of study particularly related to the future of humankind, even compared to other areas of biodiversity research. Also, scientific research on biodiversity should present research themes that sufficiently command interest of scientists, as explained in the next section.

The biology of diversity

When I published a textbook of systematic biology in Japanese under the title *The Biology of Diversity* in 1993, I was met with severe criticism saying that science should analyze the principles of nature rather than just enumerating its diversity. I was unable to convince people that my intention in writing the book had been to seek the principles existing in biological diversity, and of course the criticism was based on the title of book without reading the text itself.

After 1992, when the Convention on Biological Diversity was adopted, biologists' interest in biodiversity grew steadily, partly because it became easier to get financial aid on research projects related to biological diversity.

Diversity is a fundamental subject for biology to explore, as organisms originated on Earth when they succeeded in achieving diversification; that is, diversity is a basic principle for sustaining the life of organisms. In the story of this book, one of the main subjects of biology is to inquire into the life of the spherophylon. In the Convention on Biological Diversity, it was accepted that maintaining the sustainability of biodiversity for the future of human beings was a basic environmental issue. It is true that fundamental research on biodiversity is imperative if we are to understand it and develop the technology for sustainability. Even for supporting research on environmental issues, fundamental analysis of biodiversity is now recognized as one of the most important scientific subjects.

Research on biodiversity should be developed in various ways. This book mainly discusses research on species biodiversity, as this particular field of science needs to develop much more quickly and extensively. Establishing a large-scale project at a global level would promote understanding of species biodiversity for the sake of biology as well as for the sustainability of human beings as a part of the spherophylon.

4. Integrative Science

Cells, individuals, and the spherophylon

We do not always look at the entire species when researching species diversity. Naturally, we examine organs and tissues in depth, even just to learn how diverse species are. Any feature is leveraged in distinguishing between different species, as long as it can be used as a key taxonomical character. Once, prominent external features were often defined as species' characteristics, but we need features that express phylogenetic relationships more accurately if we want to trace their relationships with other species. Selecting proper features to use as key characters is a basic task of phylogenetic investigation.

Cells form the fundamental structure of all organisms. They are a universal unit, yet they are themselves extremely diverse. Prokaryotic cells and eukaryotic cells have fundamentally different structures. Even among eukaryotic cells, reproductive and somatic cells have clear differences in both their structure and functions. Animals, plants, and fungi all have different cell structures; in animal cells, the structure of the cells of nerves, muscles, skin, bone marrow, and so on differs. The term "cell" encompasses enormous diversity in structure and function; therefore, the actual organisms are naturally diverse even though they have cells as a common unit of life. Nevertheless, it is very helpful to have cells as a universal structural unit. The diversity of cells as a unit derives from the diversity of organelles as the unit that makes up cells, as well as from the diversity of the molecules that form cells. The DNA contained in cells is also diverse, which contributes to species diversity on the gene level. Therefore, diversity research ranges from the level of species to that of DNA.

As I have explained, living is a phenomenon that is demonstrated by cells, by individuals, and by the spherophylon. Talking about cells may seem a minute and intricate matter to a layperson, but the biology of cells requires an extremely integrative viewpoint, since cells are a single system made up of individual molecules and organelles. Individuals are made of numerous cells, which, as an aggregate, form specific structures and functions. This phenomenon of independent things forming a system also applies to the unit of the spherophylon, which is on the scale of the entire planet. When it includes even the spherophylon, the sheer expanse of its structure seems too vast to comprehend. It is not instantly clear where to start.

What, then, is involved in conducting the biodiversity research required to decipher the life of Earth's spherophylon? An integrated perspective is absolutely necessary, as biodiversity research cannot be completed with a reductionist approach alone. In order to determine what this means, we need to discuss specific studies. Individual analytical studies should be pursued thoroughly for their own purposes, but those purposes should always be evaluated in relation to integration. I do not mean to say that one scholar or one group must do everything, including analysis and integration. What is important here is to recognize how the object of analysis contributes to an understanding of what it means to live. That is what scientific research is about. Scientific research can be advanced by a great number of minute data contributions, even if each paper offers just a minor advancement. These contributions, minor though they may be, are vitally important to the advancement of science, and integrating them results in scientific advancement, which benefits civilization.

It cannot be denied that biodiversity has become a theme of general scientific research partly because it has become more appealing. Instead of having to discuss the matter in estimates, it has become possible to empirically analyze data, so anyone can clearly see how accurately research can be pursued. Yet, if it ends here, now that it is discussed in a language common to the sciences, there is a risk that biodiversity research may not help bring to light the phenomena of the spherophylon that show a nearly infinite expanse. If what is intended as analysis of diversity remains trapped in analysis of only the phenomena that researchers are concerned with, they are following in the footsteps of those who were criticized for taking a fanatical interest in the similarities and differences between organisms.

Biodiversity research contributes to analyzing the universal principles of living, while it also deciphers the various ways in which organisms live. We cannot analyze diverse phenomena if we content ourselves with saying they are diverse. In order to understand them, we need to decide on a model for analysis; yet a model is nothing but a model, not the entire phenomenon of living. We must not forget it is only a small part of the whole. (The whole, here, refers to the entity of life that has a history of over three billion years, as I have repeatedly explained.) Life creates history, and is swayed by the history it has created. History holds a tremendous amount of information. At every point in history, localized necessities of the moment amass to form the entirety of history. The reality arising out of this history is the spherophylon that exists on Earth in this moment. Biology aims to close in on the entity of life, and the biology of diversity purports to understand what it means to live in the unit of the spherophylon. Our current scientific logic and methods cannot decipher all of history. Obviously, the biology of diversity is not a subject that can be solved without an integrative view.

Various aspects of biodiversity research

Biodiversity research deals with a wide range of themes, which can be roughly divided into three categories: genetic diversity, species diversity, and ecological diversity. This is the classification of biodiversity that was referred to in the Convention on Biological Diversity, which is primarily geared toward environmental issues rather than biological research. Here, even for discussing scientific research on biodiversity, the three categories enumerated above are used.

The first category encompasses many facts: that diverse genes are recognized in all organisms from humans to colon bacilli; that even a single species like the mountain cherry, for example, has genetic diversity resulting from individual mutations; and that each individual has its own genes, and even a single individual has diverse genes within it (among its component cells). The fact that every species, from humans to colon bacilli, has different genes brings us to the next category: species diversity.

What is contained in the concept of species diversity is the fact that currently over 1.8 million recognized species of living things—tens of millions, in fact—inhabit Earth. They are not indeterminately diverse, either. They share a history of life that spans over three billion years, and have unique relationships with those that are closely related, as well as those that are distantly related.

The third category, ecological diversity, refers to the diversity of species that coexist in a certain area or ecosystem, living in an equilibrium state. This perspective deals with how extant species live. If we regard the planet as one ecosystem, this term overlaps with species diversity.

The term "biological" is sometimes used in the sense of "ecological," and some biologists equate biological diversity with ecological diversity. It is natural, however, that biological diversity covers the facts pertaining to a wide range of biological phenomena, and diverse phenomena manifest the basic principle of life. Biodiversity as discussed in this book mainly pertains to species diversity. Its research uses various features of organisms as reference points.

In analyzing biodiversity, the task of taking an overview of all living things and describing their differences, as well as the task of dissecting the biological structures that make up an individual into separate elements and identifying their origins and the history of their formation are both important, fundamental parts of the research. It goes without saying that an integrative perspective is necessary for biodiversity research, but this does not mean that reductionist analytical research is not necessary. Science has already proven that the reductionist method is the best technique for analyzing individual scientific facts. In fact, biology has made great contributions to unravelling the universal phenomena of life through reductionist analysis based on physicochemical methods, with DNA as its keyword, especially since the late twentieth century. This showed that life itself can be a subject of scientific analysis. More recently, the effectiveness of reductionist analysis has become even clearer as biodiversity became a subject of analysis. Observing differences between species intuitively, taking an imprecise look at all species, cannot be called a science. It becomes a science only when we recognize the diversity of the characters that are used as keys, and analyze where that diversity comes from. The biology of diversity took solid form as a science because it became possible to analyze origins through biological methods centered on DNA. Thus, a method has now nearly been established whereby the spherophylon can be reduced to its components and the resulting knowledge can be understood holistically. This method is expected to lead to the solution of greater challenges down the road.

If life can be a subject of scientific research, is there not a possibility that cultural and social sciences can also be pursued through a mainly physicochemical scientific method? If so, what kind of clue will this approach—which is a key to revealing the truth of the spherophylon—offer to solving matters of humanities and social sciences? Though understanding the life of the spherophylon is a purely scientific question, we cannot be unaware of its connections with such matters as environmental issues or resource shortages. Analysis of the spherophylon will lead to the deciphering of the current state of the Earth's spherophylon; this cannot be unrelated to the environmental and resource scarcity issues that we are facing now. Such issues are, in a way, intrinsically themes of natural sciences that deal with natural phenomena, but they are also problems caused by people's economic activities. They cannot be solved by extant natural sciences alone. How far, then, should the natural sciences approach be applied? This question is a timely and interesting one both intellectually and practically. I believe that the key to solving this question may lie in biodiversity research.

We just encountered the same problem in facing the COVID-19 pandemic: medical authorities expect to suppress human flow to prevent the epidemic from spreading, while the general population wants to continue its normal activities to support the economy. There was a need to maintain social life as usual while both suppressing the epidemic and promoting economic activity, but humans are not yet able to successfully overcome the competing demands of medical science and economics.

Analysis of species diversity

There are some steps to the task of analyzing biodiversity from the view-point of species diversity:

1. Investigation of biota (flora and fauna): a comprehensive survey and research into how diverse organisms are, and what kind of organisms live on what part of the planet.
2. Phylogenetic analysis: tracing the phylogenetic or historical relation-ships between various species of living things.
3. Discovering evolutionary mechanisms: analyzing why and by what mechanisms biodiversity is created.

Out of the three steps, the research now being conducted is 10 percent by a generous estimate, or lower than 1 percent by a conservative one, even for the first phase. It is impossible to reach understanding without recognizing all organisms. Therefore, it goes without saying that we need to spend considerable energy on the survey and research aspect. It is not just about extant species; there are also many facts that need to be uncovered about the species of the past.

We need not be pessimistic, however. It is true that the sum total of the knowledge the human race has gained since the days of Aristotle over 2,000 years ago has been to list a mere 1.8 million species; even so, armed with that knowledge, we can uncover unknown species more rapidly. Some natural hybrids have already been discovered thanks to estimates regarding what kinds of hybrids must be emerging, and where, based on existing knowledge of the parent species' characters. We should be able to discover unknown species and facts more efficiently by making more effective use of existing information, and building techniques for that pur-pose should be an interesting challenge.

In addition to specialists in this field, many lay people are interested in the diversity of species living around them. Small children are curi-ous about natural events, and are happy when they witness any novelty with their own eyes. The observations of non-professional naturalists can certainly be expected to add to our understanding of species diversity, if humans create more spiritual room to contemplate themselves.

The three steps mentioned above do not necessarily always progress from the first to the third. Even if the first step is not completed, research into the other two can be conducted, which may even revitalize the research for the first step. At the risk of overstating the matter, if different taxonomic features are recognized between two species on Earth, there should be valid research into how that difference came about. If three species are recognized on Earth, the analysis of phylogenetic relationships between the three can be a valid research theme. Therefore, it can be said that researchers who are engaged in analyzing specific features of a few species are furthering the biology of diversity. Those who study the dynamics of thousands of species might not call that biodiversity research, while those engaged in physicochemical analysis claim that mere observation of diversity in numerous species is not a science. This is futile bickering borne out of mutual lack of understanding. What is important here is to have a clear view of what it is that needs to be solved, and what needs to be discovered for that purpose.

Whether it is surveying and researching diversity, tracking the historical process of diversification, or analysis of the origin of key taxonomic characteristics, each aspect of the biology of diversity is conducted with all the force of extant science. Though more researchers are taking up the study now than before, they are still few in number compared to the sheer volume of research themes. Thus, progress is far more sluggish than expected, which tends to cause anxiety among researchers.

CHAPTER
5

❄

THE SPHEROPHYLON AND HUMANS AS
AN ELEMENT THEREOF

1. The Lives of Humans and Nonhuman Organisms

From humans as one species of living organisms to people and civilizations
When we discuss the life of plants, we sometimes say, "Plants are alive, too." Behind this statement is the consciousness that we, as human beings, are alive. That is why we add the "too" in that sentence. Are humans different, then, as organisms, from plants or other living things? Are we special among organisms? When we compare the differences in the basic phenomenon of living between humans and plants, there is none. Both humans and plants are among the living things that share the history of a three-billion-year evolution that started with the emergence of the first life on Earth, and are made of the universal unit of living—that is, cells—and carry out life as a component of the spherophylon. Furthermore, the life of humans is not essentially different from that of plants and other organisms in that humans deposit their living characteristics in macromolecules called DNA to pass on their genes to the next generation, and form a structure that is made up of the building blocks of cells to maintain life. That is why studying colon bacilli helps us gain a tremendous amount of universal knowledge on life. This is the basic method of life sciences through the physicochemical approach. There is nothing to contest this. That being said, human life is still different from that of colon bacilli. The facts about life revealed in research on colon bacilli must apply to all living things. Yet research on colon bacilli cannot reveal everything there is to know about life. This is exactly where the biological significance of biodiversity lies.

Humans, in particular, are unique organisms. When life was generated from inanimate things, life-forms learned how to pass on life from parents to children through the intermediary of DNA, which are self-reproducing macromolecules. Here, the fact of life acquired history. Even though the atoms that make up a life-form are quickly replaced by other atoms of the same element, and even though individual life-forms have only limited lifespans, the life that passes through these life-forms lasts eternally, accumulating historical changes called evolution. That is how the fact of life is created and passed on, forming the spherophylon.

Among the components of the spherophylon on this planet, special creatures called humans have evolved. They are primates of the family Hominidae; the family of humans (Hominidae) appeared over several million years ago, and then the extant humans, *Homo sapiens sapiens*, eventually evolved some two hundred thousand years ago. Humans evolved as a numerous species on Earth. These creatures developed intelligence, became conscious of their own lives, and created culture and civilization,

Fig. 6 Information and life

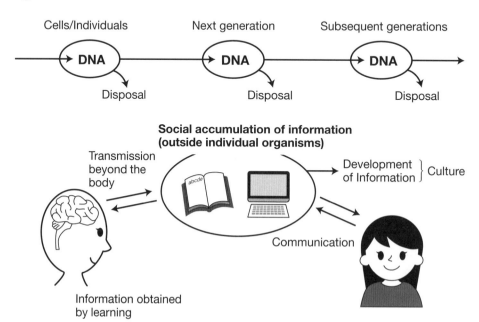

developing a way of life different from other species of living things. Those other creatures are not different from humans in that they all insist on their species' distinctness, and place their own species separately from nature, which consists of other species. Yet humans, with their culture and civilization, are set apart from nature, and in this, they have evolved into something unique, unlike any other species. (Physiologically, the DNA arrangement of the human species only differs from that of the chimpanzee by less than 2 percent.)

Animals learn in some ways to have their habits. Learning often happens while they are young, and parents often pass on knowledge while they raise their children. Animals demonstrate specific behaviors, some of which are passed on to the next generation through learning in that animal's society. These are not finished after each individual learns them, but are passed on to the next generation in society—not via DNA. This is a new method for species to accumulate historical facts that are not ingrained in their DNA. We grow up learning from our parents. Animals learn their habits, which are particular to each species, from their parents' behaviors.

Humans learn and communicate a significant amount of information. This has a lot to do with acquiring languages. We devised ways to communicate knowledge to each other using language, and to record it in writing. Thanks to words and letters, humans rapidly acquired a tremendous amount of information from learning, accumulated over time. Both mammals and birds have something comparable to language, and if we limit the topic to information communication alone, plants have methods of responding to inorganic and organic conditions in their environment. There is no other method of information communication, however, which is as accurate, or as voluminous, as human language. Studying the methods by which other living things communicate may be helpful for learning about the origin of human communication, but it is not very useful in making it even more advanced. Needless to say, only the human race records information by talking and writing (noting it in the brain, on paper, and in computers).

It can be said that, due to communication and the accumulation of information, humankind acquired something more than what could be acquired from simply living as an organism. The act of learning itself might not have been qualitatively different in comparison to other living things, but the growth in the volume of information must have brought about a shift in quality, too, considering that human society became able to pass on such massive amounts of information acquired from learning. What humans created from all that learning is what is called artificiality; what emerged from that is culture.

People alter the planet's environment when they utilize artificial means to deal with nature. Our acts affect our lifespans, and we arbitrarily create our living environments. Escaping from the state of natural existence, we live a life that is based on artificiality. Humans have evolved into a species that holds a singular position within the spherophylon. Living things acquired an historical existence that was different from the physicochemical phenomena occurring between inorganic things by depositing genetic information in macromolecules called DNA; it can be said that something similar occurred in the evolution of the human race. The act of socially accumulating historical achievements through learning can be seen among many animal species. But can we not say that the human species succeeded in multiplying these achievements by inventing words and letters, and evolved to a stage quite different from other living things due to such quantitative success in the transmission of information? This different stage is the world of culture. Any existence that advances transcends the biological concept of species.

Life as people recognize it

People became aware of their own lives. We have learned how to maintain and manage our lives, and even extend our lifespans, using technology that is quite distinct from nature for its artificiality; that is, medicine. Plants also heal themselves when they are injured; they develop wound-healing tissues (calluses) and activate the totipotency that all cells are equipped with from the start to close the wound and protect themselves so that there

122

is no problem with the life of the individual plant. Animals are prepared for wounds in that their blood can serve as a disinfectant and congeal for protection, and new tissues grow to close the wound; they have an immune system that repels foreign bodies attempting to enter the body. Here, some may say that the medicine acquired by human civilization is just a quantitative supplement to what already existed, rather than something new added to biological phenomena. Nevertheless, there are striking differences from other living things.

Human life as managed by medicine has departed far from that of diverse species in nature. This is because we single-mindedly pursued the prolonging of individual human lives for as long as possible. We became deeply engaged in acts that went against nature, by attempting to extend our God-given lifespans. Is it from a self-defense instinct that we try to escape the fear of our own death, and of those around us, our families and friends? (Such self-defense is clearly recognized in behaviors of higher animals, and even plants have an advanced mechanism to maintain the lives of closely related individuals, rather than only protecting their individual independent lives.) People made various efforts in the development of medicine, trying to put off death as much as possible by any means possible. Medical measures have successfully prolonged the average human lifespan to an extreme extent. We have taken various measures to prevent and contain the risk of death. We have driven ourselves for the purpose of protecting the human life, escaping the fear of our own death and the deaths of those close to us.

We are now at a junction where we must rethink the question of what a person's life means. If someone's life is maintained artificially, does it mean they are alive as a human being? It might become possible to acquire immortality, if artificial medical technology advances sufficiently, permanently overcoming death. Is that really what people want, though? Would it make them happy to obtain immortal life? Why did people first start seeking to extend life, even departing from the laws of nature? Living the life endowed to us as one component of the spherophylon, and passing it on to the next generation—doesn't this constitute the role of individual living things?

One of the fundamental differences between human life and that of organisms other than humans is that people are conscious of their own lives. As Rene Descartes (1596–1650) declared, "Cogito ergo sum." Human life is life that is recognized by people. In this sense, there is a marked difference between human life and the life of nonhuman species. (Though they may have culture and civilization, do they possess consciousness of life in the sense that Descartes meant?) If we are alive because we are aware that we are alive, what is the life that dwells in the body? In the first chapter, we defined living things as beings that deposit life into vehicles of life. Living does not end with the end of an individual life. The death of an individual is simply the processing of the dregs after the vehicle has passed on life to the next generation. The recognition that the individual was alive is inherited stoutly by the next generation; the recognition of life does not end with one generation, either, but is accumulated over history. Therefore, life is not finite in one individual, but is eternal, either for humans as a species, or for the people who built human culture. All living things, as beings living moments of eternal life, construct the present, moment by moment, as a component of history.

Yet people are afraid of death. People who became conscious of their own lives seek escape from the fear of death more than they seek to maintain life through biological defense mechanisms. Maybe this question—why the consciousness of life leads to anxiety over death—is in the realm of culture rather than biology. When did humans first become aware of their own lives? Living things other than humans also avoid death instinctively; this is only natural for evolved organisms. But animals that demonstrate conspicuous death-averting behavior do not do so to protect their lives with clear self-awareness of life (the consciousness described by Descartes). They act to sustain life and avoid death as part of their life activity, just as plants seek out water, light, and nutrition to live.

In contrast, people clearly are conscious of being alive. As discussed earlier, we are alive because we are aware of being alive. If we did not have this recognition, we would not ponder what it means to be alive. We would not explore the meaning of life. Biological life is not the human life. (This is no longer in the scope of biology—if we compartmentalize disciplines, it shifts to the realm of philosophy.) By this logic, does it mean that someone who is in a state of brain death is not living human life? Does it mean that those who are in a vegetative state, only able to maintain life activity with artificial support, have departed from nature, and are no longer living the life of a living organism as it exists in nature? Consequently, is such a person no longer alive as a person, or as a creature that exists in nature? Still, they are regarded as humans who are physiologically alive.

Because they recognize their own lives, people know the dignity of human life. Seeing the lives of living things, people extend their reverence for life to the lives of living things in general. Yet, when it comes to actual living, we believe it is for our own sake, reverting to the natural state of living things. No matter how passionately we talk about our reverence for the life of living things other than humans, if it threatens the lives of humans—or more precisely, our lives as individuals—we have no qualms about annihilating the threatening life. Has there been anyone who is against obliterating a pathogen from the face of the Earth in order to eradicate smallpox? Is there anyone who insists that efforts to eliminate a dangerous bacillus called E-Coli O-157 from Earth go against reverence for life? No one would hesitate to end the life of organisms that are not conscious of their own lives in order to maintain the human life that we each recognize.

The life that people recognize is the life that the human culture recognizes, and we cannot expect to understand it fully through analysis of biological life, which aims at understanding how life is formed and how life activities are maintained. When biologists discuss how we recognize life, they are referring to the examination of the brain's biological functions. There is no school of biology that deals with the dignity of people as historical beings. Even so, can we really declare that human life is discussed and dealt with clearly separately from the lives of species other than humans? Our stance on life is quite ambiguous in various regards.

This is because various aspects of life are diverse. Diversity and ambiguity, however, are the true form of life when it is actually lived. For that very reason, it is often the case that we cross wires when we are having important discussion about life.

Human life controlled by people

People became conscious of their own lives through fostering culture, allowing it to become divorced from nature. Now, we partly govern our own lives by artificial technology of our own devising. People control life according to their consciousness. In an extreme case—the death penalty, for example—we sometimes intentionally determine the fate of life with premeditation. (In animal society, it is not uncommon that an individual that disturbs the order of society will be killed, but here we will refrain from seeking a prototype of human behavior in animal behavior, delving into themes of animal sociology. Let us just mention that the life and death of people is not left to natural phenomena any longer.) Even dying is not left alone nowadays.

Prolonging life is the most characteristic way to escape from the fear of death that civilization has devised by artificial means. People's lifespans have been extended excessively due to medical intervention. What are the consequences?

Living things, in general, live as vehicles of life; once their reproductive behavior has been carried out, they are naturally done with their lives as individuals. I should think that the human lifespan was naturally around 50 years or even shorter before the advent of civilization. This is because our reproductive years happen in our twenties and thirties, and having produced the next generation means that our main role as living things in nature has been completed. Needless to say, some species have many individuals that are not involved in the production of the next generation. In bees' society, worker bees are not directly engaged in the reproductive act. They work to gather food, fulfilling their role in the division of labor, so that the queen bee and drones can dedicate themselves to procreation without a care in the world. That is how the society of bees as a whole manages to sustain the life of its species.

Since people succeeded in extending the human lifespan, we do not come to the end of our lives as individuals after 50 years; we continue to live to age 70 or 80 on average. It became necessary to create a social role for the elderly, as they have already done their duty of producing the next generation. They therefore found a new significance in contributing to culture and civilization. That is how the society of the aged was formed. But if the job of creating our successors has been accomplished by the age of 40, life after that is superfluous for ordinary living things; for a species, living extra life means wasting resources. (Is the life of a worker bee a waste of necessary resources or the species? The form of the species' existence sustained through its social life is a basic biological fact, which can be also seen in the society of cells such as *Volvox*. If we view the human creation of culture and civilization as another process of evolution, the prolonging of life can be understood as one way of living that exists in nature.) In fact, the quantity of resources and energy that people consume has become immense, in parallel with the development of civilization. We consume a great quantity of fossil fuels, which consist of energy captured and accumulated in the geological age, because using solar energy that can be captured now on Earth is not enough. It is the choice of humans to enjoy extended life, and I do not mean to discuss it here. Yet, if the consumption of energy grows immensely, surpassing the amount necessary to sustain the species, we need to have policies to compensate for that. Among families and nations, when expenditures grow large, income is secured to cover it. So why do people pretend it is not their problem when it comes to a problem of the human race?

The human lifespan is under people's control, nowadays. Because of this, it is far removed from the life of an organism in nature. This being the case, we need to understand it correctly, and treat the modern human lifespan as artificial life. It is dangerous to remain under the illusion that the human lifespan is natural. In that sense, too, cultured people, though historically originating in the species of human beings, have become unique among species living in nature.

The lives of nonhuman organisms

What is this thing that is called reverence or love for the life of organisms on Earth, and where does it come from? Do we love nature because we think it is beautiful? Most people do not love something wholeheartedly if they find it ugly. Attractive animals and beautiful plants are cherished, but insects and bacteria that harm our pets are exterminated, and weeds intruding on a garden of beautiful flowers are ruthlessly pulled out. Maybe people did not originally have love for organisms in general. Were we taught to cherish all things by religious doctrines? If so, what kind of rationale is behind the teaching that we should love all living things on Earth? Does it come from the sense that human life coexists with the lives of a diversity of organisms, which we had even before we recognized it as a fact? Maybe the knowledge that humans and other species share the process of evolution is in our blood. But let us not assume here that we perceived such things instinctively.

At this time, there is no denying that we cherish living things other than humans partly because doing so proves useful for us; they may be valuable as genetic resources, or essential to the human environment. At the same time, however, the human life that has continued over nearly four billion years of evolution knows to cherish our comrades who share that history with us. How can we love ourselves without loving brothers of our own blood? Does this not mean that eliminating organisms harmful to our lives is the same as severely punishing those we love when they commit wrongful acts?

It is people that recognize the fact that other creatures are alive. Those creatures do not become aware of the fact that they are alive. It is not that they exist because they are aware of it, but because people are aware of it. If this logic is valid, that awareness of others' existence itself leads to our affection for other living things.

Here are some examples as food for thought. Ginkgoes are the only remaining species of Ginkgophyta, which prospered in the Mesozoic era. Humans oppressed the relatives of ginkgoes and drove them to extinction. The same human race, however, somehow held the extant species of *Ginkgo biloba* in awe. Our ancestors planted ginkoes in temples and shrines for spiritual reasons. Ginkoes, on the verge of extinction in nature, became protected by people, and now provide benefits to them as genetic resources. (This account of ginkgoes' survival is just one interpretation; it is not verified as fact.)

We have an ancient Japanese poem (haiku) that goes like this: "Treading mountain path, I found a violet somehow so dear." This poem appeals directly to our sentiments, not to the mind. What lies beneath this charm? Our acts of selecting, discarding, or protecting diverse species must derive from our calculation of how useful they are to us. But it cannot be only the useful ones that we hold dear. Did we not originally have this affection for all living things as our companions? We must have had to eliminate those—the root of evil, as it were—that had to be disposed of. That has to be the sentiment of human beings as living things. Somehow, when we only care about the benefit and harm they offer us, our actual view regarding creatures other than humans becomes markedly distorted.

Understanding people properly

Human beings are one species of living things. There is much to learn from other species in exploring human life, since we only have limited knowledge of people. The behavior of monkeys, a closely related animal, offers many examples to us. By studying other species as research material when we could not experiment on humans, we uncovered numerous facts. Still, facts that can be learned from other species are facts that apply to those species, after all. Let us remind ourselves: the phenomena found in colon bacilli are common to all living things, but learning everything about colon bacilli does not teach us everything about life. It is important to recognize that humans, in particular, which evolved in their own unique ways to be different from other species, have in their singularity especially marked differences from others than the variance usually found between different species. We cannot conclude immediately whether or not this is due to the fact that humans have philosophy.

Analogies between humans and other species are, after all, only that—analogies, not homology. The forms of knowledge that humans possess may be understood in many respects through the knowledge and experience that other species have. However, the skills humans possess for communicating that knowledge to other individuals far surpass those of other species in quality in some ways, even if such communications are fundamentally universal among living things. And even if such universality can be found in the brain, the difference between humans and other species can be measured by quantitative differences in the degree of the brain's development. We can also say that if the absolute amount of accumulated time is the same for humans and other individual species, it will be perceived completely differently from the human perspective (the same amount of time can mean totally different things in terms of its ratio to the life cycle: think of the speed of generational change for colon bacilli compared to the time it takes for humans to go through one generation).

The brain is said to integrate a human individual. Surely it is the brain that controls the behavior of humans as animals. Not only conscious actions, but also unconscious reactions are under the brain's control. This is why understanding an individual completely is considered to be the same as understanding the brain. Even so, can we say, for example, that muscle cells are not of primary importance in forming an individual human? There is no human that does not have muscles. Can we say that individual cells do not matter? It is true that the cells that are in your body right now can be replaced by other muscle cells. It is an undeniable fact, however, that the cells that you possess right now form you. Humans are particularly outlandish among the components that make up the spherophylon of this planet. Are humans to the spherophylon as the brain is to an individual? Can we say that each pine tree of a forest is not that important? From a human perspective, the world is human-centered and the human race is something special. From the perspective of a mountain tree, however, humankind may be just another component of the spherophylon, and not particularly special. It is just that this particular component has become gigantic and tyrannical, like a cancer cell, endangering the very existence of the planet's spherophylon.

People believe consciousness belongs to individuals; yet the knowledge developed by a certain individual into a specific form is retained and communicated to others; it becomes a common asset of humanity, and is no longer a personal possession of that particular individual. Here again, we see individuals as those who make momentary contributions to eternal life, and live in the present moment of that eternal life. While people have personalities and individuality that is complete in itself, that individuality serves as one component of the spherophylon on Earth, just as every single cell of the trillions of cells that form a human individual serves as one component of a multicellular organism with their own individualities.

2. Nature and Artificiality

How natural is nature now?

The antonym of "nature" is "human-made" or "artificial." Something that contains a touch of a human act cannot be called purely natural. People admit that they are beings that are inevitably opposed to nature. We are that confident in our own actions. It is not difficult to understand "nature" as a word, but it is extremely difficult to clearly understand what pure nature is. This is because artificiality is hard to grasp.

Humans originally evolved as a creature (*Homo sapiens sapiens*) of the natural world. Until humans became people (that is, they developed culture), they were just one animal species without any particularly striking singularity. Human behavior was not considerably different from that of wild animal species, such as lions and tigers, until people created civilizations that opened the door to artificiality. When humans developed a unique civilization and enhanced the quality of their behavior dramatically, it became necessary to create special terms—"artificial" or "human-made"—for human behavior, as it was no longer within the scope of animal behavior. For example, we never say, "lion-made" or "tigerficial." On an individual level, lions and tigers are quite strong compared to human beings, though these strong wild animals do not destroy our environment and bring our Earth to a desperate crisis.

Did humanity exit the life of living things in general, going over some threshold? It seems difficult even for specialists studying hominization to decide when artificiality started. Primates that acquired bipedal walking eventually evolved into humans, and the actions of humans are called artificiality.

Shifting from hunter-gatherers to farmers in the Neolithic Age, humans turned into beings opposed to nature; they forced considerable change on nature by creating aspects that were against nature. Hunting and gathering, no matter how thorough, are part of the food chain in the world of plants, animals, fungi, and microorganisms (i.e., the biosphere). When they started farming, however, humans cleared ground for agricultural land and pasture. Earth's surface was dealt a decisive change, though on a small scale initially. It was the first step for the actions of people—human acts, in other words—to start creating a dichotomy on the surface of the planet, in the nature around them. Then people started controlling some of the creatures that were living in the wild: the beginning of domesticated animals and cultivated plants.

I do not intend to embark on a historical discussion about when and how human acts began artificiality. It must be that the accumulation of small changes eventually reached a level that could be called hominization, rather than starting definitively on some date. Instead of delving any deeper into the matter, let us just state the fact that people have built civilization to the current level, where anyone regards the terms "human acts" and "artificiality" as antonyms of "nature."

Then the planet's surface was modified, on a small and large scale, by human activities, for 25 centuries even after the start of the New Stone Age. There is not a single patch of Earth that has not been affected by the artificial actions of the human race. It follows, then, that there is no pure nature left on Earth, if what is affected even slightly by human acts cannot be thus regarded. What is normally called nature is not genuine, nor primitive nature; it has been influenced by human acts, though it may still retain considerable natural character. In this book, we should define the term somewhat more precisely.

I believe that some species of plants were possibly formed through human-made activities (Iwatsuki, 1997; also cf. 2 items ahead). Humans were originally a species that was part of the biodiversity that makes up the world of nature, but they have become independent of nature, changing to something that is opposed to it, since they became able to use artificiality, which opposes the natural world. Some organisms started to form species under the influence of human activity. Even for a long time after this shift, people did not let the dichotomy come to the surface, and succeeded in coexisting peacefully with nature, keeping the consequences of human activities localized. Now, in this era of globalization, human activity is conducted on a global scale. We switched from containing the consequences to the local level to expanding them to the global level. The clash is fully exposed, with fangs and bared teeth.

Globalization is not to blame. We must predict the effects of the expansion of certain activities, deciding on which ones to expand globally and which ones to contain. That is why we need a slogan like, "For coexistence between people and nature." Humans, as one component of nature, were originally simply part of nature, and did not have to seek to coexist with it. The fact that we now have such expressions shows that we have become divorced from nature and are keenly aware of the need to live with it.

Before going further, I would raise two points for comment in this section. The first point is the difference between terms "humans" and "people" here. I intend to define humans as a species of animals under the scientific name of *Homo sapiens sapiens*. The term "people" should be defined, on the other hand, as those with a civilization that has formed an intellectual society. The second point relates to the term "nature" as it is applied in Japan. The Japanese term equivalent to "nature" is *shizen*, a word that originated from the Chinese philosophy of the Tao. This Japanese term usually includes artificially modified sites that are similar to nature. In Japanese English, we even say "secondary nature" to refer to artificially modified green sites. In the descriptions in the following section, I will use the terms people, humans, and nature carefully, though I am afraid that I may cause some misunderstanding by misapplying these English terms.

Artificiality in human life

It is impossible for modern people to conceive of life that is removed from human acts and artificial factors. We would not be able to continue living if we erased human acts, which are unnatural factors, from our daily lives.

When did people's lives become opposed to nature? There may be some who still lead lives attuned to nature. Conversely, some people had already begun unnatural artificial activities even in Paleolithic times. What about Japanese people? The beginning of farming was indeed a great attempt to exert influence over nature, forcing drastic change on it. Are we able to say that Japanese people, who are awed by nature and love it, conducted such human activities in harmony with nature? (Though you may well complain I interpret Japanese people's actions favorably because I am Japanese, this actually has to do with the environment of the Japanese archipelago in which people lived. It has just recently been determined that the Paleolithic age in North Japan continued for nearly 100 centuries, though the lives of Paleolithic people were fairly different in the early and late eras. They seemed to very gradually develop their own lives in opposition to nature.) Even Japanese people, however, overdo unnatural, artificial acts these days. We have a house to live comfortably in, garments and accessories to adorn ourselves with, and especially food to meet our insatiable gastronomic desire; as a result, we hardly have any leisure to be immersed in nature.

Let us take a closer look. Mornings start with numerous unnatural artificial acts; we wash our faces and brush our teeth with a lot of toothpaste—much more than necessary. Hardly anyone thinks about this artificial product flowing out in the drain and contaminating the water. In winter, we wash our faces in hot water, hating the cold, which is a waste of energy.

Then, we have a hurried breakfast before going to work or school. You may like Japanese food or Western cuisine; either way, you eat a bowl of rice or a slice of toast—and rice and wheat are both grains. Though they are plants, both rice plants and wheat are completely artificial, a far cry from their wild ancestors, which did not dream of the changes to be undergone. A morning meal often comes with eggs. These eggs also have nothing to do with wild birds. When the chicken was first domesticated, it roamed outdoors and had lean meat. At some time since then, broiler chickens, which are as tender as tofu, became prevalent, and eggs became a sort of artificial factory products produced by chickens in cages. There is no need to go into butter, milk, seaweed, and pickles. When we put on clothes made of high-quality wool, it reminds us that we owe them to sheep. We obtain wool from sheep that are artificially raised en masse at ranches. If your clothes are made of cotton, think of the cotton plant, though you may never have seen one. We could go on, but this is enough to show that your life is divorced from nature.

Does the modern way of living make those species happy—those rice plants, wheat, chickens, cows, cucumbers, sheep, and cotton plants? They used to enjoy their own lives in nature on this planet, having undergone their own processes of evolution. Now that many years have passed since they became domesticated, they no longer live autonomously. They are completely under human control. Some may say that this is why they live a comfortably secure life, protected from the harsh wilderness. This, however, is just like the rhetoric of former colonial powers that boasted of giving the people they subjected rich lives, though they deprived them of freedom and exploited them thoroughly. (I will not discuss the fact that slaves in human society are quite different from domesticated animals.) We did not give those species a way of life that they desired. Just as people do not live by bread alone, wild creatures are natural only when placed in nature. Humans placed wild animals and plants under their control, and even placed themselves under human control, evolving into beings that cannot survive in genuine nature.

This note seems to come up often, but I would not say that these poor cultivated animals and plants should be returned to nature. Since people have altered our way of living to what it is now, we must live our lives at the expense of other creatures. I only discuss this topic here because I want to clearly present how aggressive to nature, and how thoroughly unnatural, human life has become. I am not here to discuss whether it is right or wrong. If we say it is evil and we do not want to be involved in such heinous acts, we have no choice but to stop living. For people who have constructed civilizations, it is no longer possible to revert to being primitive humans (*Homo sapiens sapiens* with no advanced civilization) living in primeval nature.

Going back to nature

There is a movement for people to live in harmony with nature. An extreme example is an eccentric religious group that refuses any medical treatment, which caused a stir after going bankrupt. Refusing to receive even medical treatments—which are artificial, human acts—seems aligned with nature. Yet even these people do not eliminate all artificiality from their food, clothing, and shelter, or the minimum necessities of life. So they remain in an unnatural state for much of their everyday lives, but exclude specific human acts, including medical intervention. It is not possible to accomplish a return to nature in such a state; yet they try to be thorough by adopting a method that even deprives people of their lives. This is simply wrong.

Surprisingly often when we discuss nature, we dissect it and discuss whether its individual fragments are nature or not. Does the anti-artificial act of refusing medical treatment really come from nature? Medicine has not departed from nature on its own. Medical acts have evolved to protect people's lives, as part of people's efforts to construct human acts, in a fundamental deviation from nature (it must be added, however, that we cannot declare that all human acts conducted under the name of medicine are good). Here, I would like to discuss nature as a whole, not some recognizable fragments of natural elements.

A complete return to nature is not something that is within our reach at present. Restoring the conditions of primeval nature that existed before humans became people is not possible for the human race; it has already been living a human life opposed to nature for a long time. It may be theoretically possible to turn back the DNA sequences of all living things to what they were a few dozen millions of years ago, but such technology may become available only in hundreds of years' time. Therefore, full recovery of nature can be said to be impossible, and even if it were achieved, it would be made possible by artificial acts. Nothing can be returned to its previous state in history. What has once been produced cannot be undone. We must realize the importance of acts that take time. We cannot seek to go back to primeval nature. It is at least possible to simulate primitive nature, but how should we discuss its pros and cons? Is it not a simulated experience of bygone days that we seek in doing so? It is great to learn from the past, but the future is what we create. History is not reversible. If the past was beautiful, we can create something that resembles it, but it is up to us, people who live on Earth now, to determine what form it should take.

The impact of civilization on the diversification of plants

I published a book in Japanese (Iwatsuki, 1997) under the title "The diversification of plants under the impact of civilization." The details may be consulted there (or in a Chinese translation accomplished by Dr. Lin Sujuan in 2001), but a brief summary of it will be given here.

The speciation of wild species is a slow process even for sexually reproducing animals and plants, which succeeded in evolving rapidly over a period of just millions of years. In contrast, people began cultivating plants and animals only as recently as the past two millennia or so. Therefore, cultivated animals and plants are regarded as outliers created from wild species in nature for the convenience of people, rather than distinct species generated by the natural phenomenon of speciation. They are products of human acts, and not wild species in the world of nature.

Since civilizations developed, plants that are called weeds have thrived in areas surrounding human residential areas. These plants originally lived only in naturally disturbed areas, but advanced into the human environment and made it their habitat, since that artificial environment happened to suit their preferences. This means that weeds thrive under the protection of humans, but are quite vulnerable in the world of nature. Weeds prosper under the shelter of that great giant, people.

Unlike weeds, however, there seem to be certain plants that have actually generated new types in accordance with the new environments that people created. These are called (wild) plants cultivated by civilizations. It might be hard to believe that such plants exist at all. I said above that it takes millions of years to form a new species. It simply does not add up that there are wild species that created new lineages (species) in the history of a human civilization that is a mere ten thousand years.

Let us analyze the activities of plants, then. It is sexually reproducing populations that take millions of years to form new species. Of course, sexual reproduction is the most effective way for living things to conduct speciation rapidly, particularly animals, plants, fungi, and others that are highly advanced in their structures and functions. Therefore, organisms that reproduce asexually (i.e., primitive groups) require an even longer time for speciation. This has been borne out by the history of evolution.

After human civilization developed, causing dramatic alterations to the planet's surface (destroying nature), how did new plant species form within a mere ten thousand years? As it would take a whole book to explain this accurately and minutely, I will give you an overview.

My specialty is the systematics of fern plants. Some ferns, like *Dryopteris erythrosora* or *Pteris cretica*, are believed to have formed new species induced by human civilization. These species conduct a special type of reproduction called agamospory (or apogamy, a form of apomixis), abandoning sexual reproduction and developing into species that are different from the maternal genotypes. These plants managed speciation in hundreds of years through combinations of simple mutations. The above-referenced book is not to discuss the processes through which such speciation occurs or what the pros and cons are for plants. Here, let us just suggest as a provisional conclusion that human acts can have such consequences.

In addition to the speciation of agamosporous strains, we can refer to plant speciation combining hybridization and polyploidy. These types of speciation, which occur through normal sexual reproduction, may be called a rush evolution. Further comment will not be given here on asexual reproduction, which includes all vegetative reproduction, as it relates to speciation events.

3. Human Life and Nature

Is it really true that nature is an essential friend to people in their lives? What is meant by "nature" here? Let us examine pragmatic issues and more fundamental ones separately. The pragmatic issues include those related to genetic resources, as well as those related to the preservation of the human environment.

Genetic resources

We seek the resources necessary for us to live on the products of nature. Diverse organisms form a circle of life that can be called the spherophylon and sustain life as phylons (lineages) through mutual dependence. Humankind, as one component of the spherophylon on Earth, is no exception as one species of living things.

When technology reaches a totally different level, it may be possible to produce life's necessities with solar energy, without using any organisms. When that becomes reality, will our meals be contained in pills? Would we be happy with such meals? They could be tastier than what we have today. Anyway, that is just a possibility now, and we cannot expect this to be a solution for the issue of hunger in the human race on this planet today. For the time being (though no one can predict for how many centuries it will stay this way), we have no choice but to develop a way of living that depends on the products of nature for the necessities of life. The global population exceeded seven billion a few years ago, and it does not seem that the acceleration is abating yet. This in itself is problematic, and population control is a grave issue for policymakers that needs to be dealt with on a global scale. Rapid population growth, combined with diversification of lifestyles, has led to dramatic increases in the need for resources. We hear frequent warnings of the likelihood that hunger will spread throughout the planet within the twenty-first century if this trend continues. This issue cannot be ignored; we must take measures immediately.

Statistics show that three kinds of plants—rice, wheat, and corn—account for two-thirds of the total plants that the human race consumes directly and indirectly as food. The top 20 plants account for 80 percent of the total, and the top 400 plants, 99 percent. Humankind, which has fostered high-quality domesticated species and enhanced their use as resources since the Neolithic Age, has become dependent on the genetic resources of the limited number of species that it uses. These species are not necessarily among the most productive. It is likely that people who lived in temperate regions where civilization started began to rely on plants that could be cultivated in areas that were suitable for living.

If our only concern is productivity, there must be other species that are more useful. Species of living things that have become diversified on Earth are equipped with diverse genetic resources. It would be a shame not to make use of them. We did not dream of the genes contained in organisms becoming useful to us so soon until a short while ago. Therefore, "genetic resources" in agriculture meant those of species already in use, or of closely related species that could be utilized in selective breeding through cytogenetic techniques. Technologies such as genetic engineering, cell fusion, and cell culture—known to the general public under the blanket name of biotechnology—offered the possibility of making use of wild species' genes that had previously been disregarded as totally useless. If we could succeed in, say, combining genes causing good flavor with genes that were highly productive, it would not be impossible to secure resources for life's necessities for the global population of ten billion, though that might not be possible in the immediate future. The application of biotechnology in the field of breeding is now steadily progressing, though at

140

minimum there must be strict safety guarantees against the introduction of any harmful genes.

Along with developing such technology, securing valuable genetic resources is another urgent issue. Currently, a sixth of the 1.8 million recognized species on Earth would become extinct, or would be driven to the brink of extinction, if they were left to their own devices, the International Union for Conservation of Nature and Natural Resources (IUCN) warns. Those that are not recognized will simply become extinct before people name them or even become aware of their existence. Eventually, we may face a situation where we cannot source genes in nature and have to develop a new technology to synthesize new combinations of genes when we need them, even though the genes of extant species can be used very cheaply, securely, and effectively.

On the topic of genetic resources, we should be able to use the genes of all the diverse species on Earth as resources. This means that millions, tens of millions, or even hundreds of millions of species, which have been part of the spherophylon that we belong to for more than three billion years, contain infinite possibilities that are beneficial to people. People might stop wanting things from nature if human technology obtained the "hand of God" that could create anything that people might desire some centuries down the line. Yet we must remember that human life would not be sustainable if we ceased cooperating with the diverse species that inhabit Earth, sharing the spherophylon. Our race would become extinct before it could achieve the hand of God.

Conservation of the human environment
When discussing the relationship between nature and the diversity of organisms living in nature, it becomes necessary to take a look at the environment that supports human life. I touched upon this in relation to the spatial expanse of the spherophylon earlier; here, let us explore the effect that the diversity of living things, including humans, has on the living environment of people.

Various creatures living on Earth exist as a result of evolution, and are still evolving towards the future. The historical process of evolution is not history that has been played out by each species or individual, but history that has been created by the involvement, whether direct or indirect, of all living things on the planet, including humans. Therefore, the sphero-phylon has a system complete in itself, just as each individual member of extant species has a system complete in itself. (The planet Earth has one spherophylon, but I wonder how many equivalents exist in the universe. Guessing at the number should be a job for space scientists.) The human race evolved as a member of the spherophylon, but it became opposed to nature in some aspects since humans created culture by gaining con-sciousness and recognition of their own lives—in other words, since they became people. No other species on Earth is so marked in its conflicts with other species. Nevertheless, humanity has not completely lost its character as a component of biodiversity. It has not completely escaped from being a component of the spherophylon even at this moment (and it does not seem that people would agree to do so).

The spherophylon is sustained by complex mutual relationships (most still unknown to human culture) played out by species that are currently estimated to be in the millions, tens of millions, or even over a hundred million. Just as the death of particular cells in an individual does not deal a decisive blow to the life of that individual, the extinction of some spe-cies will not affect the survival of the spherophylon. What will happen, though, if more than 10 percent of species go extinct? Our science is not able to give an accurate prediction, but here is a fact: a certain ecosystem sustains or repairs itself even when biodiversity is degraded if it maintains a certain level of diversity, but the whole ecosystem suddenly collapses if diversity falls below a certain threshold. This threshold varies, and it has not been discovered what it is for the planet's spherophylon—that is, how many species' extinctions it can withstand.

Following this argument becomes very much like a discussion of how far biodiversity can be reduced. Is it a discussion of biodiversity as an envi-ronmental issue sound when it is based on the premise that biodiversity must be lowered? Rather, should we not discuss the ethics of degrading it now? It is inevitable that our anti-nature acts will increase as long as people live, which unavoidably oppresses nature and leads to reduced biodiversity. Should we not try to build science and cultivate technology from the viewpoint of ensuring people's survival, rather than degrading nature? If, with that purpose as the premise, we discuss the right way for people to live in relation to biodiversity from a scientific standpoint, we cannot but conclude that it is a sound policy not to deviate from the natural state in the evolution of organisms. We should assert that it is impossible for today's science to predict how much degradation the world can survive. The purpose of science and technology should be to keep the deterioration to the minimum.

Reverence for life

It is comparatively easy to gain people's understanding of how important nature and biodiversity are to us in terms of material gain, and so we must at minimum mention profit when we discuss the necessity of maintaining biodiversity. However, we should not be preoccupied with that angle when discussing this matter. The difference between the characteristics of people and those of other organisms can be sought in the fact that people developed a culture of awareness of their own lives. How, then, do nature and biodiversity interact with human dignity, our self-awareness of life?

Numerous species that form the spherophylon alongside humanity have lived through a history of evolution going back more than three billion years. Just as the cells that make up an individual have complicated mutual relationships with each other, allowing some cells to repair the individual when other cells are harmed, the species that form the spherophylon on Earth have mutually supplementary cooperative relationships from sharing the history of evolution. What place do humans have in those cooperative relationships?

People started recognizing their own lives and becoming attached to them. Other species, too, may fear death, but our fear is incomparably solid and immense. We greatly fear not just our own death, but also that of our loved ones. That sometimes leads us to place greater importance on those we love or are close to, which may even lessen our sense of guilt in sacrificing others for the sake of ensuring our own safety and that of our friends and families.

Having become conscious of their own lives, people now pit human acts against nature and consider themselves exceptional beings in nature. People are aware of acts that are beneficial to humanity, and behave in ways that are different from how they behave toward other species. It is true that other species also recognize species other than themselves in some ways, but not as intelligently as people recognize themselves. Accordingly, other species react to other species differently than humans do.

We do not have uniform relationships with other species; they vary greatly according to the species. Those who find roses beautiful and cherish them diligently pull out weeds that grow near rose bushes. Those who love dogs use potent drugs to eliminate the pathogens that cause skin diseases in dogs. Both the weeds and the pathogens are living things, but we take markedly different actions toward them. We confront those who attack the creatures around us that we love. This biased, human-centered love of creatures is something that we cannot avoid as long as we exist as living things. If that is emotion that people naturally have, can't there be empathy for all the living things that make up the spherophylon?

Those who love roses and dogs regard people who do not share the same passion for roses uninteresting, and view the habit of eating dogs as diabolical. Even so, they kill other animals to feed dogs, and they eat cows and pigs themselves. People need to eat something to subsist. Some people—vegetarians—do not believe in eating animals. Though vegetarianism is not a uniform school of thought, it does not make much sense to me that they are willing to eat plants but not animals. Even worse, some believe that they should not eat vertebrates, but invertebrates are OK. From a biological standpoint, this is preposterous, though we should not criticize other people's personal beliefs and values.

As long as people live, they need to eat, and must kill animals and plants for that purpose; this in itself is the very meaning of life. (People did not choose to live solely on dead organisms like saprophytic plants, or decomposers. In that sense, it may be that vultures, which scavenge only dead bodies, have more reverence for life than people.) I have no intention whatsoever of proposing that we should establish a way of life that enables us to survive without killing creatures for the sake of protecting the life of the spherophylon. My take on this is that we should explore how people should live, accepting the way of living that we created as we evolved.

We kill living things for food; killing for survival must be called a necessary evil, if killing a creature is evil without exception. As it is evil, albeit necessary, it goes without saying that such an act should be carried out with a certain moderation. Attempting to stamp out harmful organisms for the sake of self-preservation—this needs to be defined as a necessary evil, if killing is evil. If we know killing is evil, then we can conclude that taking more lives than necessary is unmitigated atrocity. What, then, distinguishes a necessary evil from a pure evil?

Even though we grew into people from human beings and became able to have an objective view of biodiversity, humankind still needs to coexist with a legion of species to sustain its life. In that sense, the affection we have for other living things can be called fellow feeling. People sometimes sacrifice fellow beings, though. Our bodies, which started from a single fertilized egg to reach an aggregate of trillions of cells by repeating the processes of cell differentiation and generation, remove parts that are diseased and send those cells to death in order to protect the remaining majority. We cherish the living things around us, but if they happen to threaten our existence, we drive them to death. Our love of creatures can be quite selfish. The technology developed by human civilizations may even make preemptive attacks on harmful creatures, giving higher priority to self-protection, even though we may sometimes have fellow feelings for them. Civilizations have established such methods, while other species would not go that far.

The narcissism of the spherophylon on Earth

Our reverence for life is for all species of living things. We all are fellow beings that have evolved through mutual relationships and gather together to form a single spherophylon. Then, our having reverence for all species means that the species called human beings, which is an element of the spherophylon, respects the components of the spherophylon living on Earth, including itself. This is ultimately revering and loving itself in the form of spherophylon.

People take care of themselves. We treasure our lives, and take very good care of every part of our bodies so that none of them get hurt. We do not cut out parts of our bodies that we do not like. We cherish ourselves as a whole, as an individual, or in the parts that make up that individual. Self-love is called narcissism; this comes from a Greek myth, in which a beautiful young man called Narcissus was mesmerized by his own reflection in a pond and drowned; the flower called narcissus sprouted there afterwards.

There is a term, biophilia, which denotes reverence or love for life. This is about loving the life of each component of the spherophylon's life—that is to say, self-love of the spherophylon living on Earth: narcissism, in a word. Loving all living things—animals, plants, fungi, microorganisms, bacteria and all—is not at all putting oneself under restriction for the love of them, but loving all parts of oneself that constitute the spherophylon, which is the wisdom of someone who lives within the spherophylon. No one neglects any part of their own body. Therefore, reverence for life may be another expression of self-love, or celebration of narcissism.

Narcissism is usually explained as an attitude held by people, but every organism has a tendency toward narcissism—a fact that is actually demonstrated by the history of evolution. Every organism is an element of the spherophylon, and its narcissism in loving itself is, at the same time, love for the spherophylon. This narcissism of the spherophylon is performed in reality by all the organisms on Earth; in this way, the spherophylon can steadily carry on living a healthy and happy life forever.

146

CHAPTER
6

✢

LIVING THE LIFE OF THE SPHEROPHYLON

1. The Reality of the Spherophylon on Earth

The life of the spherophylon

We usually consider ourselves to be living as individuals, but here we have learned that at the same time we—that is, each individual organism—are living as an element of the spherophylon. On which side, then, will our consciousness of living fall?

When there is pain somewhere in the body, we usually consider it an injury of the body, not just of the place where there is pain. We treat the pain or injury by applying medicine to that particular point, and we expect the body to recover from the damage.

When the spherophylon has a wound somewhere, how do we react to it? The site of this injury may be a particular species when we consider species diversity, or a particular nation when we consider the international society of humans. Damage to a particular species refers to a species considered endangered due to our recent environmental issues. The extinction of a particular species is recognized by experts as a threat to biodiversity or to its environmental equivalent on Earth. When a particularly lovely species goes extinct, people often miss it sentimentally, though we should recognize more clearly that this extinction is a clear sign of the deterioration of biodiversity on the Earth, and we should realize that the spherophylon has been seriously harmed at that particular point. In the same way, when a nation in the world is going to be destroyed, the balance of international society is endangered; in this way, too, the life of the spheropylon is attacked.

In everyday life, people view their own life as belonging to them, and their colleagues' lives as belonging to their colleagues. Human life is different according to the individual concerned. A person has their own life, and they are responsible for it. Likewise, their colleagues are responsible for their own lives. With this understanding, people make efforts to improve their own lives. Generally speaking, people who make greater efforts meet with greater success. When everyone in society tries to live as best they can, the society is seen as having a healthy economy as well as a sound culture.

Competition among individuals usually leads to positive growth of a society, though it often leads to imbalance between its members. People in a society have inequalities. One person may have better ability, and another may have innate weaknesses; even if the two put forth the same effort, the results will be different. Even when they have nearly the same ability, their success will vary depending on the fortunes they meet on the way. In a modern society, it is not possible for everyone to live under the same conditions. This is the diversity of people's lives in society, and no one can control social inequalities. Here I am discussing both human society as well as the spherophylon that comprises all organisms on Earth.

Understanding the Earth's spherophylon

The New Systematics field of botany proposed by Julian Huxley (1887–1975) and the New Morphology proposed by Herman Johannes Lam (1892–1977) were much discussed in the 1940s, due to the challenges of developing research techniques to overcome certain barriers. Both of them influenced researchers at the time, but they were forgotten as biology made great strides forward, mainly through the physicochemical approach. It is inevitable that new approaches with new terminology eventually disappear if they cannot construct something new. The approaches proposed in the 1940s brought something new in terms of perspective and analytical techniques, but they did not have the drive to induce stable development, as diversity research itself was losing its position in the world of biology. In that sense, the results determine whether proposals to surpass the extant science actually succeed or turn out to be a flash in the pan.

As for the biology of diversity, this field lost its central position within the discipline in the late twentieth century, being regarded as altogether outdated. It contributed to accurate accumulation of information by describing phenomena, but could not overcome the technological barriers preventing it from determining the underlying universal laws. This does not mean, however, that the importance of the discipline was forgotten. This is something that I personally became keenly aware of in my research. There were always high expectations for diversity research in biology, but it just could not manage to live up to them. Then the biology of diversity suddenly made progress, adopting reductionist approaches that it had not been able to make use of previously; this, along with the advancement of analytical technology in biology, enabled it to suggest the right course for biology to take.

This course is to study the life of the spherophylon further, in order to gain a correct understanding of what it means to be alive now. As this subject is almost like an aggregate of individual phenomena, it requires setting of the correct parameters for analyzing this massive subject, so that research into biological diversity does not remain a mere accumulation of individual research.

I have explained in detail what the spherophylon is and have admitted that we know little about its reality. Even so, I try to encourage people to care about the spherophylon on this planet. We need to have more extensive knowledge of what Earth's spherophylon is. In terms of time, it can be partially gained by tracing the phylogeny of living things, and in terms of space, by uncovering the structure and functions of the biosphere. These are the very subjects of science, and not accessible to everyone. Yet they become the foundation for a correct understanding of what it means for people to be alive now.

I have already discussed the fundamental research to some extent. Let us take a quick look at what has not been achieved and what is required in relation to the dissemination of the information that has been acquired so far.

The most fundamental research in the study of plant species diversity is a survey of what kinds of plants grow where. This survey focused on flora; though regional floras are frequently catalogued, it has become quite difficult to catalog the flora of the world nowadays, as the amount of information is tremendous. However, there is a great deal of interest in information assembled on a global scale, and researchers are asked to compile information in easily accessible ways. Therefore, the world's major plant diversity research institutes came together to form the International Organization for Plant Information (IOPI) in 1990, for the purpose of putting together existing information to compile a catalog of the world's flora. It called on researchers of this field to help collect information and build databases in order to provide services that could be accessed easily by both researchers and the public. This project has now expanded to an intergovernmental organization, the Global Biodiversity Information Facility (GBIF) founded in 2001. Its mission is to organize all the information available concerning biodiversity; as of 2020 it had collected more than two trillion entries.

It is vital for this type of project, too, to promote the compilation of individual regional flora. In Japan, projects to compile the flora of Japan in a database were initiated, receiving subsidies from the Ministry of Education, Science and Culture; the latter is a project of the Japanese Society for Plant Systematics. The most recent Flora of Japan publication was initiated in 1993 and completed in 2020 (Iwatsuki et al., 1993–2020).

In addition to the compilation of existing information, collection of further information is another urgent matter. Japan, however, does not have a permanent international organization to conduct research on species diversity and to help compile and provide information. Hence, a proposal was made following deliberations at the 1990 Commemorative Foundation for the International Garden and Greenery Exposition in Osaka, Japan, to establish an organization that would create a database of plant information and provide general access to it. This project was named BoSSCo. Another project called GaiaList 21 was proposed, led by the Zoological Society of Japan, to found a large-scale research institute somewhere in Asia under Japan's initiative. Its aim would be to decipher all information on all living things on Earth with the collaboration of researchers in related fields from all over the world, and organize it into a generally accessible form. This would include not just basic information as described in museums, but also information on genomes disclosed in as much detail as possible. Though uncommonly large-scale, this project is essential to bringing to light the reality of the spherophylon on Earth. As explained in chapter 5, biodiversity is extremely important as a genetic resource, as well. Therefore, it is necessary to collect the information that has been acquired and make it available for general access. A preparatory committee is working to establish a natural history museum in Okinawa, as described on the homepage of Okinawa Prefecture.

A spherophylon for each time and location

The aggregate entity called the spherophylon, which was formed over the course of a long history, has extraordinary structures and functions, with all factors playing their part in optimum ways. Individual organisms live their lives as efficiently as possible, while they properly play their appropriate parts as components of the spherophylon. Living things show extremely high diversity in locations such as humid tropical forests, and extremely low diversity in deserts and similar areas. They follow a way of life that is best adapted for their habitats.

How adaptive creatures are in the process of evolution and speciation is not something that can be lightly touched upon in this book, so I will just lay out arguments that are more or less regarded as conclusions, fully aware that they do not sufficiently cover the matter. Most mutated genes are unable to survive. They are usually not discarded, but are preserved as inferior genes that are not reflected in the expression of characteristics. Only a limited number of mutations form into adult characteristics of species that survive as living things. Only those species that are able to choose a way of life best suited to their time and location have survived on Earth. You then may wonder why a species might go extinct. I would draw your attention to the phrase, "best suited to their time and location" here. The habitats of the planet's spherophylon are never static for an instant; they are always changing. Forms that are best adapted at this moment may no longer be so the next moment. Therefore, the immense number of species that may reach the tens of millions includes those that are struggling to live even as this moment passes. Conversely, the spherophylon is made complete by including such species. (Analogy is not always the best explanation, but if we compare the entity of the spherophylon to individuals, the cells that form an individual are all perfectly streamlined as cells, but they undergo death and birth. We are reminded of this every time we scrub our bodies, have our hair cut, or trim our nails.)

The spherophylon, which leads a highly organized way of life with a long history of continuous, uninterrupted evolution, is only complete when it comprises perfectly tuned components. Humans also were born on this planet in that history; they were perfectly shaped to be a component of the spherophylon. (I feel some chagrin in using the past tense here. Is this because I regard myself as one of them? I might feel more at ease if I thought of myself as one individual among the infinite living things that make up the spherophylon, and as an aggregate of trillions of cells, which are the smallest unit that living organisms can be reduced to.) Humans, however, changed into something different, and are threatening the solid stability that the life of the spherophylon established.

What evolution brings to the spherophyoon

Living things are historical beings; in the other words, the life of every organism has a background going back nearly 4 billion years. This is not necessarily something that all people grasp. As a science that analyzes the historical aspect of life, biology includes the fields of evolutionary biology and phylogeny. No longer an academic term used in biology in the previous century, "evolution" has entered the general lexicon, gaining wide use. It is used to discuss the evolution of the planet or the universe, or of society.

152

The diversity of living things involves facts that contain an immense volume of information, and so theoretical discussions must come first in generalizing it. Therefore, the study of evolution, which is the historical element of diversity, has been centered on theoretical observations until recently—as indicated by the term "theory of evolution." Only with the recent progress of analytical technology in biology, and with the help of physicochemical approaches, has it been possible to explore the historical process that creatures have lived. The term "evolutionary biology" has come to bear significance, as it is now empirical rather than theoretical.

The theory of evolution tended to be regarded as quite conceptual, rather than a purely biological subject. It was even discussed as an ideology. That may have been not without a certain merit, but it did sometimes invite misunderstanding among those who regarded biology as a modern science. Even not a few biologists themselves seemed to be convinced that species historically became only more advanced, though they became fed up with fierce discussions in the name of evolutionary theory. (Some still enjoy the study of life phenomena as a conceptual subject.)

The word "evolution" originally meant development and expansion; it was sometimes used in biology to denote development in ontogeny. With concepts such as Jean-Baptiste Lamarck's theory of use and disuse inheritance and Charles Darwin's theory of natural selection, people in the nineteenth century came to recognize that species do change and diversify; when the diversifying phenomenon of living things became a subject of biological research, the term "evolution" came to be used specifically to signify the phenomena of speciation and diversification of species. (When "evolution" was translated into the Japanese language, *shinka* was chosen as its translation. This word strongly connotes advancement and progress. This is partly why Japanese people tend to understand evolution as the advancement of species when discussing evolution in Japanese. It is likely that a majority of Japanese, outside of specialists in evolutionary biology, understand the word "evolution" as meaning change into something better or of higher quality, not only more adaptive.)

Darwin explained the phenomenon of evolution as "descent with modification," and it is interpreted exclusively as change in France, too. Living things continue to change historically; in other words, they change gradually over generations, with the accompanying phenomenon of diversification. That is evolution in a nutshell. It is estimated that life was generated on Earth more than three billion years ago, and the historical development of life has fostered diversity since then. The study of evolution is thus the study of biodiversity, and the concept of progress is not called for here. It is a fact that life-forms generally became more complex and highly adaptive over their three-billion-year history. On the other hand, not a few organisms have evolved into life-forms that are not necessarily more advanced than before, as in the examples of extant prokaryotes, and they enjoy life as it is in their own ways. (I hasten to add, just to avoid misunderstanding, that extant prokaryotes are organisms that contain the history of more than three billion years. They should not be considered the same as the prokaryotes that lived more than three billion years ago, though they may look alike. Prokaryotes, like humans, are creatures with the entire history of evolution embedded in them; they just do not show that change in conspicuous ways.)

We should note here that living things are historical beings. We do not just live in this moment as individuals; we are beings that were born on Earth as a result of the phyletic evolution of organisms over the course of more than three billion years ; we form part of the biosphere of this planet and walk toward the future that leads to eternity. That history is ingrained in the life that courses through our bodies for our keeping. Let us go back to our starting point as the life of organisms and remember this. We have long since lost the sense of history in our everyday life, which is spent on day-to-day worries. That is why we need to have a clear, solid understanding of the historical significance of our present existence, so that we can live fully today. The actions we take today will be embedded in history as time elapses, and will leave a mark that can never be deleted; we owe that much responsibility to history even at this moment. In that sense, I believe we may be able to make our lives more historically meaningful by learning that we live today as a moment in history. That begins with correctly understanding what we are, as one of the organisms called humans, in the process of the eternal evolution of living things.

2. The Healthy Life of the Spherophylon

Nature conservation and human activity
"Conservation of nature" is a strange expression. Nature is the antithesis of artificiality, which denotes human acts. As human beings, we are opposed to nature in our very being. Setting aside the fact that people were originally products of nature, let us organize the facts around the dichotomy of modern people and nature.

As long as people exist, it is inevitable that they will create and develop artificial factors; it is impossible for modern people to eliminate them. People cannot revert to the state of humans before they developed civilizations. It is not possible to completely undo what history has constructed. Therefore, the only solution for eliminating artificiality is to annihilate the human race from the face of the planet. But who would insist on doing that in order to protect nature? (I will overlook here any fundamentalists who believe that nature is much more important and valuable than human beings, who are after all just an element of nature.) If our goal is the future prosperity of humankind and peace on Earth, we should instead make effective use of artificial factors. We should promote human activity that is antithetical to nature. The term "conservation of nature" comes with a caveat: "for the sake of humanity." From this perspective, it only follows that nature that is not beneficial for us should be wiped out. Nature, however, has significance as a whole, and it is no longer nature if part of it is removed. The aim of conservation of nature, then, is to preserve as many aspects of what used to be nature as possible. One might ask why we should go to such lengths to preserve nature. Is it not possible to create a completely artificial environment in place of nature? In fact, people in urban areas are surrounded by mostly artificial environments. They still live comfortably enough.

Roaming over the hills and relaxing on the beach, people can have a getaway, away from the hustle and bustle of the city. European people have the custom of going on a vacation for certain period of time in the summer, leaving behind their regular working life. It is true that we can forget about our daily woes and find peace of mind in places where some aspects of what used to be nature remain. Is this our natural state, though?

What about modern resorts in Japan? Young people who cannot stand the serenity of nature bring in artificial noises even to these places. It seems they are simply bringing urban hubbub to a more spacious location, so their nature vacation is nothing more than just getting away from a cramped house or apartment in town. What is nature for these people? Resorts represent a typical example of the destruction of the natural environment for the sake of people when they stage nature while excluding vital factors such as plants and animals. Are humans taught so easily to depart from nature? Are the young people whose activities alienate them from nature really a new breed of people? Can we arrange comfortable environments consisting artifacts, entirely estranged from nature? Perhaps only an outdated breed of people seek peace of mind in the tranquil hills and seaside. If so, what does protecting nature mean to the new breed of human race?

Protecting the eternal life of the spherophylon

Is it not possible for the organisms that evolved into particular life-forms called humankind, which has unique civilizations, to become completely attuned to nature? Are they fated to destroy nature through their artificial activities? People are creatures that act on their own will. They can produce the effect of artificiality to suit their wishes. Should they not have a clearer awareness of what they seek and the direction they are headed for? Should they degenerate into unbalanced creatures with a lifestyle in which they only exploit resources from their surrounding environments for immediate gain, despite having highly advanced technologies?

No one, even those who advocate conservation of pure nature, would insist on being perfectly faithful to biodiversity while excluding people.

156

For example, no one would propose sacrificing human lives to protect the life of pathogens, even if they were infected by them. If an outbreak of E. coli O-157 infection occurred, no one would suggest that we protect it because it is a product of nature. No one would be happy to have their kitchen infested by cockroaches and rats. (I would pass over the ideas that E. coli O-157, cockroaches, and rats have evolved in adaptation with human-life and are not quite natural in the purest sense.)

What does conservation of nature mean, and what is it for? In chapter 5, I explained that people cannot live completely divorced from the natural environment. What should we protect and what should we let go of in order to ensure we have an environment to live in comfortably? There will always be something that we have to give up. In order for us to survive, we will have to sacrifice some creatures, no matter how much reverence we have for the life of all living things, as our actions will be ultimately premised on our desires. If someone were opposed to killing creatures that threatened people's lives, I would like them to propose their ideal way of life.

As I have said, people cannot live without forcing modifications upon nature. Therefore, what we must consider in land development is how to preserve as many natural elements as possible. This is a logical conclusion, as we cannot survive without them. How much nature could be left alone, and how much should be destroyed so that the land can be developed? If there were policies on this matter, we would only have to follow them, but science has yet to discover what they would be. That is why it is imperative that fundamental research should be immediately devoted toward developing them. If we were able to estimate exactly what would happen to nature in the future as a result of modifications we made today, we would be able to observe human activities without feeling disquieted. In reality, we do not know what consequences our actions would have, so we must be circumspect in our actions. How far into the future can we say we foresee?

We cannot wait until we have a perfect outlook. People have various wants and desires in their daily lives. The more than seven billion people on Earth each insist on their right to live, seeking affluence. No one could ask anyone to languish under hunger and illness until we arrive at the perfect policies, when no one knows when they will become available. We cannot but proceed with development of the natural environment in order to make our lives more comfortable. What kind of policies can science present to us today? It is sheer negligence not to present policies, even provisional ones, that are suited to the day. The policies could be wrong, and so it follows that we should opt for safer ones that are less likely to give rise to later problems.

It has to be admitted that it is impossible to conserve nature 100 percent, if we want to continue to survive. There is hardly any primeval nature left on Earth in the first place, as nature has been greatly influenced by one civilization after another throughout history. How far should we proceed with the development of the planet's environment through human activity—the antithesis of nature—and where should we stop? The question here is what kind of guiding principle should serve as a policy in this matter.

What helps us reach a conclusion here is the image of people aiming to coexist in harmony with nature. Why harmonious coexistence with nature? This is self-explanatory. We must try to maintain the spherophylon—which exists on Earth, forming a unified system—in its entirety. Would anyone choose to cut off parts of their bodies? Would you sell one pound of flesh off your chest? The spherophylon lives as one entity on Earth. It is the duty of people, who are the brain and the heart of the spherophylon, to sustain this life-form perfectly. This mindset can be called reverence for the life of the spherophylon. If some part of the body is afflicted by a disease like E. coli O-157, we do not hesitate to remove the cause in order to maintain ourselves as individuals. We remove it, as we should if we find something that could be identified as causing a disease in the spherophylon on Earth. Some may say that this idea of maintenance of the spherophylon is too human-centric; I only say that people, who inherited civilization, recognize their own lives in the process of thinking, and that the life we discuss now is the life that people recognize.

Disease prevention for the spherophylon

Some people accuse us of being completely ruthless against pests and pathogens, though we talk about reverence for life. This is nothing but a strange false accusation.

People usually take care of their bodies and their lives. We follow the old Chinese classic saying: "This body of mine, its skin and hair, is a gift from my parents. It is the first of my filial duties to keep it safe from harm," and we have narcissism, or self-love. That is why we do not hesitate to eliminate anything harmful that emerges in the body. If a tumor is formed, we immediately have it removed to prevent it from spreading. Yet tumors are also one of the groups of trillions of cells that form an individual, which all started in a single fertilized egg. Although they are part of the body, no one would cherish a malignant tumor or cancer, saying it was part of the gift from their parents.

The same goes for the spherophylon. It contains various harmful bacteria and pests, not to mention E. coli O-157. Some people may protect cockroaches, mosquitoes, and flies and let them breed inside their houses, cherishing their life; we may let that pass as their choice. If they tried to foster a cancer inside their bodies, however, it would only be a kindness to warn them of the consequences, at the risk of meddling in others' affairs. Most of the species that form the spherophylon are elite, and friendly to us, but some of them could be hostile to us. We should remove those at an early stage, as we would a disease inside our body, in order to maintain the eternal life of the spherophylon on Earth. Reverence or love for its life does not extend to the lives of all organisms. It is sometimes necessary to make hard choices to protect the permanency of this planet's spherophylon.

This is a human-centric argument, of course. As you, readers, must know by now, the eternal life of the spherophylon on Earth is here regarded as something that exists for people. Therefore, it is only natural that this should come across as selfish and human-centric. People have already made major alterations to the spherophylon for the sake of their own survival. If we were to focus on the survival of the spherophylon from the same standpoint as other living things, as just another species, it would not be possible to return history, which is irreversible, to the point in time before civilizations began.

If we care about the sustainable maintenance of the life of the planet's spherophylon, we should take a hard look at whether we have in fact become the cause of a disease. If humans are propagating at an unnatural rate like cancer cells in the spherophylon, they need to be removed at an early stage. It is possible for us to turn ourselves into its cancer cells, whether consciously or unconsciously, and it should also be possible for us to stop it when we detect the danger. We must have an accurate understanding of the situation. We should also take preventative measures so that we do not proliferate unnaturally like cancer cells, in the end becoming a threat to ourselves as well as the spherophylon. That is the intelligence that people, the self-appointed Lords of Creation, should have.

Harmonious Coexistence between Nature and Humankind

1. The Progress of Technology and Civilization

What is technology?

In an authoritative Japanese dictionary, *gijutsu* (the term used to denote technology) is defined as: "1. The art of doing something dexterously. Technique. Workmanship. 2. The art of putting science to practical application to modify or alter objects in nature and make use of them in human life." Let us consider the meaning of this word in the second definition. What is noticeable is that it defines technology as something that modifies or alters objects in nature. Further, this only applies to human technology, as the definition mentions the application of science. This calls for a little more deliberation. Let us get back to this later.

Humans (*Homo sapiens sapiens* in nature) became people (having civilization), and people developed arts that were called artificiality (as shown in their words) as a result of their activities. This was nothing other than technology, as it modified or altered objects in nature. As technology progressed, it brought civilizations into existence, which were, as the definition suggests, inevitably opposed to nature. When the human race, which had been a species of animals, a primate of the family Hominidae, became people and built civilizations, they turned themselves into beings that were opposed to nature, defining themselves as anti-natural (that is, artificial) beings.

Technology is a product of human activity, and applying it to nature is the very act of destroying nature, since applying artificiality—which is defined as the antithesis of nature—to nature is by definition preventing nature from being as it is.

In discussions of the conservation of nature, we often see arguments that are hostile to technology. Some avid conservation advocates assume that technology is the root of all evil; if we seek to preserve perfect nature, all artificiality must be eradicated; therefore, technology needs to be annihilated (I shall not reiterate the argument about whether perfect preservation of nature is possible now). It is not possible for those who live in human society, whose civilizations are thus highly advanced, to live without technological progress. It is not possible to return the state of things back to a previous point in history. It is a fact, as I have pointed out on various occasions in this book, that misguided use of technology has proven detrimental to the survival of humanity. Technology is not to blame, however; it is how we use it. There are many cases of erroneous use of technology leading to the destruction of nature. It is not possible to sustain the eternal life of the spherophylon on Earth without further developing technology and using it appropriately. In this chapter, we will explore what technology means to people, and what is required of it now, for the purpose of maintaining the life of this planet's spherophylon.

Technology and science

Technology puts science to actual use. In the Japanese term *kagaku gijutsu* (literally "scientific technology'), science serves as an adjective for technology. In Western languages, "science and technology" may form a phrase, but not a compound word. Originally, this Japanese idiom was intended to denote science and technology, though in actual use it means technology developed by scientific progress.

If we regard technology as something that we use and build on to make it more effective at enriching our lives and protecting us from enemies, we had it even before humans became people; in a broader sense, animals in general have it. Technology in this sense is not an exclusive property of humankind.

When humans began to make use of fire, they acquired the skill to light fire, to extinguish it, or keep it burning. When they first made stone tools, they learned how to flake a stone to make a tool out of it. When they went hunting and collecting, they had the techniques to hunt animals and to collect nuts and fruits. Such technologies were not significantly different from those that monkeys and other animals had. They were originally passed on from the days when humans were not so different from monkeys. Living things, not just monkeys, have the ability to learn something from scratch by themselves in their lifetime, and to learn from watching their elders in their social life.

In the meantime, science involves seeking to acquire new knowledge through scientific methods, triggered by people's intellectual curiosity about the nature, principles, and mechanism of things. This is a singular activity that is not demonstrated by other animals; it is one of the human acts that define people. Just like the creation of art, it is an intellectual activity that is specific to people.

Where did science and art originate? Art began in ancient times, as can be seen in the Altamira Cave paintings (Altamira Cave is thought to have been painted 15,000 years ago; Grotte Chauvet, found in 1994, is still older, purportedly painted some 32,000 years ago). As for science, we can trace how scientific thinking became established after people started keeping written records; some say natural history began with Aristotle. Yet, people must have had intellectual curiosity much earlier than that. It may be that it only came to be organized as science in the era of Aristotle. In any event, science began when people acquired language and writing, becoming able to pass on the intellectual heritage amassed by society, along with the cumulative history passed on by DNA, and to store these assets on an incomparably large scale. This occurred only after civilizations had already elevated the human race, a primate of the family Hominidae, to being people.

Since people began scientific research as a form of intellectual activity, they discovered various laws and principles of natural phenomena. Such scientific insights were the major driver of spectacular technological development. In order to develop technology, we tried to promote science, which formed its foundation, but this was quite the wrong way round when you think about it. It is true, in some ways, that we needed to learn the laws and principles of nature in order to develop technologies that would enrich our lives, and that led to the beginning of science. In many cases, necessity for technological development induced scientific progress. Every war brought about exponential advancement in science. Even so, epoch-making progress in science often comes from research conducted purely out of scientific curiosity, rather than out of technological interest. People engage with challenging scientific themes due to their intellectual curiosity about nature's laws and principles, and the anticipation of the joy of solving them. They cannot be expected to make great contributions to science as long as their research interest remains practical. Upon such scientific discoveries of the laws and principles, we gain significant technological development. If scientific research studied natural phenomena for the purpose of technological development, it would be nothing more than analysis of more or less limited subjects.

Science and art, which are products of thought, are exclusively human property. Coming into possession of the intellectual property called science, people brought technology up to a high level, applying scientific principles to it. This is what is called *kagaku gijutsu* (scientific technology, or technology based on science). Technology in general is common to living things, but highly advanced technology, called "scientific technology" is something that only people can use. More recently, it is this type of technology that is referred to by the term "technology" (by this definition, the expression *kagaku gijutsu* is a tautology; adding a science-related adjective to technology, which is based on science, is redundant).

Japanese people in particular, tend to believe that science and technology have the same origin. The roots are slightly different, however, between science—which is a purely intellectual activity—and technology, which is a pursuit of practical benefits.

I would add a short note here. A thousand years ago, science was quite poor and contributed little to technology. People at that time had fairly

164

advanced technology and produced a variety of tools, especially for use in daily life. We find beauty in the folk craft produced by the technology of the average person in those ancient days. The beauty of folk craft is highly evaluated as an art form. Thus, technology advanced much earlier than science did, and did so in parallel with art; this is also recognized in relation to the fact that all the animals have their own technology to sustain their lives, though they have no scientific information at all to support and promote their technology (see below).

Progress in technology

Since the days of stone tools, human technology has reached a level where nothing seems impossible. Seen in this light, the present and the future of human civilization and the technologies that support it seem rosy; there seems to be nothing to be pessimistic about. Nevertheless, we become critical of the anti-natural acts that accompany technology when discussing harmonious coexistence between nature and mankind. This, however, cannot be taken as a criticism of technology itself. The problem lies in how technology is used, and for what purpose. Some seem inclined to believe that all technology is inherently evil. This argument would ultimately condemn humans, born as creatures of the world of nature, since we cannot live without modifying nature with technology due to all these previous alterations made over the course of history, and we have been using basic technology since before humans became people.

Alfred B. Nobel (1833–1896) invented dynamite, which gave literally explosive impetus to human technology. He amassed a great fortune, and so could have lived his life happily, content with his achievement, until the end of his days. Dynamite, however, came to be used in warfare, proving greatly effective for massacre. Appalled by this, Nobel decided to establish the Nobel Prize. This well-known fact gives a very important insight into science and technology since the very beginning of the twentieth century. The Nobel Prize played a major part in promoting science and technology, but various "dynamites" were invented in the process. Were they always used for peaceful purposes? Weren't some of them used to oppress nature, threatening the survival of humanity?

Science makes progress for its own sake, but this cannot be said of technology. Technology in most case is developed with the intention of using it for some purpose. That is why wars can trigger remarkable technological progress. People confront their enemies in a life-or-death situation. They do not hesitate to inject any amount of money and labor into war efforts in order to win. It is symbolic that technology progresses by leaps and bounds in such a situation. This is related to the fact that technology is sometimes used for misguided reasons: how did weapons of indiscriminate murder like poisonous gas and explosive mines come into being?

Except for such special cases, there are not necessarily many cases in the history of progress in technology in which technology in itself is to blame. It is only that there are more than a few cases where some things, like dynamite, were originally invented to benefit people, but came to be used for the opposite purpose. We cannot be too mindful of this in relation to technological progress. We know very well that nuclear technology may help human society greatly, though using it for evil ends, or carelessly, would destroy our only Earth.

Scientific technology and seafood

I am borrowing here an idea shown in an interesting essay by Mr. Tetsuro Hara (1995) in a PR journal from The Biohistory Research Hall.

A fishmonger sells red snapper and octopus. These are both types of seafood to be eaten by humans. There is that distinction here. In biology, however, red snappers and humans are both vertebrates, while octopuses are mollusks, which differ considerably from vertebrates in their phylogenetic relationship. Red snappers were in the same group as humans until relatively recently, but octopuses evolved into creatures different from humans at an earlier point.

There is science and technology, and there is art. We group science and technology together under the discipline of natural sciences (in a broader sense), and art is placed in the category of the humanities. Technology, however, is something that humans already possessed when they behaved in the same way as other animals, while intellectual activities like science and art were created after humans became people; that is, they are artificial outcomes (figure 7).

This explanation by Mr. Hara is very clear. So I shall pursue this thought a bit further, following his lead.

Animals do have technology (though it bothers me that technology in this sense is slightly different from the dictionary definition). Not only animals, but plants also make various devices that are effective for surviving. However, the kind of technology that people developed to the extent that it opposed nature was highly refined, making effective use of the laws and principles of nature that people had deciphered through intellectual activities called science. The technologies that fostered human civilizations came into being when people established them on the basis of science. In that sense, modern technology is necessarily scientific. That is why science came to be expected to develop as the foundation of progress in people's technology. People started talking about "useful science." Phrases like "useful science" and "scientific technology" are like the broader category of seafood. From the standpoint of natural classification based on historical development, science is closely related to art. When we regard science as something that supports the foundation of human civilization, "scientific technology" is a valid term. It actually may be surprising that this idiom is unique to the Japanese language.

Even so, science originally comprised intellectual activities, much as the arts do. Technology is useful for enriching people's lives, a way of seeking fulfillment in life different from the pursuit of happiness in intellectual satisfaction. Because people pursue science and arts that are conducive to intellectual activities as hobbies, Japanese people believed for a long time that both scientists and artists should suffer honorable indigence. The highly advanced, complex science of today, however, is somehow beyond the capabilities of a single scientist. As it requires a large-scale project to see results in many cases, it often takes much more than the effort of individual scientists. Therefore, human society needs to deliberate on how to develop science further. At present, this is far from being accomplished, which makes me believe that we are far from ready to sustain and develop the life of the spherophylon on Earth.

2. What Technology Brings About

What technology gives us

Artificiality is, by modern definition, in conflict with nature. It sets human acts against unspoiled nature. I wonder if human-made objects have at times been evaluated more highly than nature itself. People built what is called civilization by developing artificiality. Therefore, civilization itself is anti-natural. Humanity's intelligence lies in the creation of civilization, which is antithetical to nature in principle, attuned to nature, rather than warring with it—to have it coexist with nature.

When people switched from hunting and gathering to farming, they transformed a great expanse on the Earth's surface in order to develop land into farmland and pasture. This was the first large-scale destruction of nature by human activities. Trees were cut down to clear the forests for agricultural fields, though it took a long time to have wide areas of cultivated land. Burning the forests was one of the simple and affordable developments of forests in early time; slash-and-burn cultivation is different from fired development and continuously performed even now in some areas.

On a global scale, however, it was contained to a very limited part of the planet, although that part was thoroughly ravaged. Because we enhanced productivity substantially, we did not have to make modifications to much of the land, avoiding confrontation with nature on a global scale. Furthermore, we managed not to deal a devastating blow to nature, as we induced the transformation gradually.

Even without talking about harmonious coexistence with nature, people demonstrated it in practice as a matter of fact. We preach on its necessity now because unbridled use of artificiality has led us into unrestricted expansion of unnatural acts. When did we degenerate to the point that we need to expound on the necessity of living with nature?

Of course, the planet has been transformed substantially since the beginning of farming. The pastoral landscape is a result of the human activities conducted since that time. Scenes of rural villages that many people regard as "nature" and the home of their hearts are actually artificial. We came to mistake artificial products for nature itself. Some of the plants inhabiting rural villages are wild species that acquired new forms in environments developed by people; others are domesticated plants brought into existence by human activity.

As artificiality advanced continuously from simple tools to more advanced technologies, it became more anti-natural in nature. People built various artificial objects on Earth to improve their lives. In the end, the environment has become so oppressed by human activity that the health

Fig. 7 Different classifications

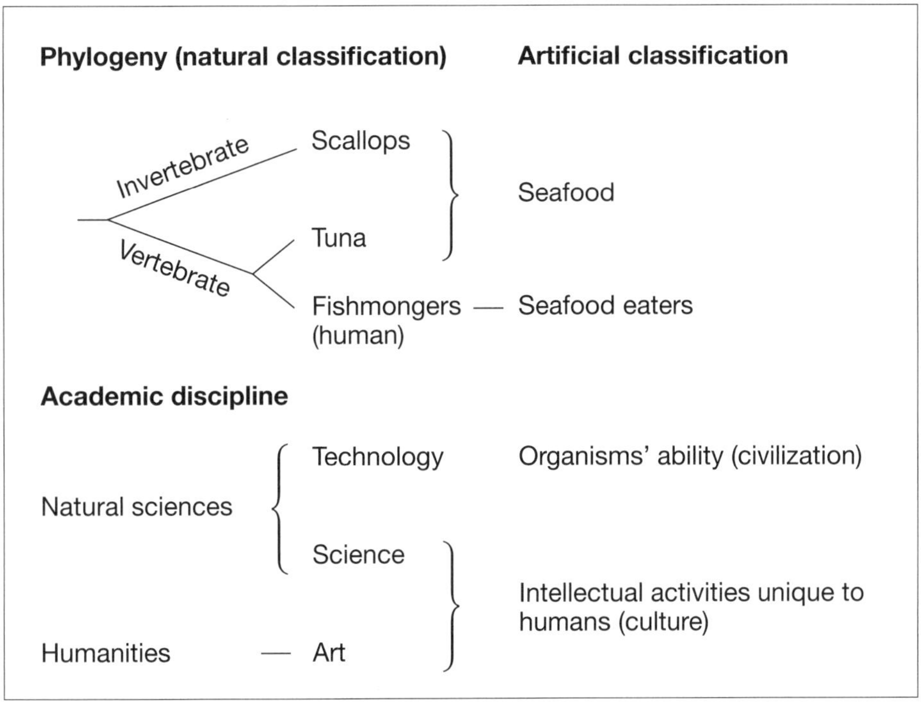

of the planet in the immediate future is in jeopardy. Therefore, we now talk about the necessity of conserving nature and making the case for living together in harmony with nature. Our Neolithic ancestors managed splendidly, but now something as matter-of-fact as coexistence with nature is discussed as if it is something new. Why should our supposedly superior technology give rise to such a dangerous situation?

Various technologies borne out of dynamite of people's intelligence were made much use of in order to improve our lives. Those technologies may be superior, but some people—though a small part of the entire population—try to use them at will for their own interests or that of those close to them, even if that causes others trouble or destroys nature. Some use good technologies in ways that are bad but merely misguided, or sometimes even nothing less than nefarious. We have learned that remarkable technologies, more than mediocre ones, have great potential for evil when used wrongly. How grave would be the consequences, if the minority of people who use technology for heinous deeds that benefit only themselves and gravely harm the planet's spherophylon had influence as policymakers?

It is often expected that the application of technology will be controlled, say by governmental policy, though it is not wise to leave regulation of scientific and technological developments to political power. The most important principle should be to use ethics developed in human society through access to information to control people's negative actions. The international regulation of weapons is among the most urgent demand faced by human society.

How to use technology

There are many ways technology can be used in error. For example, people may blatantly use it in a way that they know well is wrong, being fully aware of the consequences of doing so, simply in their own interest as individuals. Some may be compelled to use it wrongly in self-defense. Use of weapons is a typical example here.

Another scenario is misguided use caused by ignorance. Some people are neither aware of the gravity of the consequences nor versed in the rightful use of technology, and as a result, they cause undesired effects. Some may bring on disastrous situations because they do not sufficiently foresee the consequences, though they believe their use is correct. This type of misuse is often the cause of grievous threats to the planet's environment.

Who uses technology? It is not only the engineers who are the problem here. We must take a panoramic view of the use of technology that changes people's lives. Insisting on halting technological progress out of fear of misuse is an unproductive argument. We should make clever use of good technology to have positive outcomes. If the general public pretends that it is the responsibility of engineers or the job of policymakers to decide on how to use technology, there will be no end to the villains who abuse them for personal gain.

How can we prevent the misuse and abuse of technology? We cannot complacently sit on a false sense of security that it will not come to anything serious in our lifetime when we have driven the environment into the grave state it is in. When various nations have weapons so highly advanced that they pose a threat to all nations, they establish agreements that the weapons will not be used without restriction. This is because many people know that the unlimited use of weapons could lead to annihilation of the planet. When it comes to the gradual destruction of the environment, however, people have not yet grasped the gravity of the situation, so they are not very inclined to end the misuse and abuse of technologies at the cost of their own interests. A small part of the population points out the danger, but they have failed to persuade the human race. Everyone knows that nuclear weapons could destroy our only Earth, and still modern people choose to have a lot of nuclear bombs. Given the situation we currently face, we need to make arrangement to put the brakes on technological development in some areas.

I would comment here that the application of any technology should be made only when it is useful to the general population, with perfect protection against error. Based on what was said previously in this section, I can't proceed without referring to an actual example of dubious usage of technology. Based on technological advances, nuclear power plants were developed as a way to produce energy economically. These systems were also recommended as a technology for avoiding significant carbon dioxide emissions produced by thermal power generation. I am not a specialist in nuclear power and possess no more knowledge in this area than the general public. In connection with environmental science, it is urgent that carbon dioxide emissions should be reduced, but nuclear power is not involved in carbon dioxide release. However, control of nuclear power should carefully be managed, and no error, no matter how small, are allowable. As seen in the case of the nuclear power plant accident in Fukushima during the 2011 Great East Japan Earthquake, the risk of tsunami should be observed most carefully—though TEPCO, the owner of the Fukushima plant, did not admit responsibility. In any event, bringing conditions back to something like their original state after such accidents is very costly, if it is even possible. We know now that it costs a lot to ensure the safety of nuclear power from natural disasters as well as artificial attacks. Any accident, if any, has a high price, and it is now estimated that nuclear power is not reasonable compared to other means of power generation. If we are to develop nuclear power generation further, we must discuss how complete safety can be achieved, knowing that it will have a high cost. The promotion of nuclear power may only be supported by the fact that it is a clean energy that emits no carbon dioxide. There is a disheartening report, however, that TEPCO has made multiple errors in controlling the system of stations even ten years after the Fukushima disaster.

Technologists develop their technology based on scientific information created by scientists. The new technology is then implemented by decision makers who have little knowledge about the technology and its scientific basis. Modern technology has a great influence on human lives, and we should be careful when implementing new technology, though the necessary disclosure of information is generally not forthcoming and people are usually indifferent if they can enjoy good results from it. Only when people are unhappy with the outcome do they protest the decision makers

A typical *satoyama*, characterized by patches of vegetation of various ages, conserved in Kurokawa, Inagawa-cho, Hyogo Prefecture

Southern species growing through the Japanese winter

Adiantum capillus-veneris L on a grate over a water channel in northern Yokohama

Pteris vittata L growing beside a road in Hakusan, Bunkyo-ku, Tokyo

Terraced fields in southeastern Yunnan, China, above
a road that sustained damage in heavy rains

A golf course with artificially grown grass in Leigh
Creek, an artificially established coalmine town in a
desert expanse of South Australia

who adopted the new technology. When new technology is implemented by society, both those who introduce it and those who use it should carefully study all the potential benefits and risks that it poses.

The results of scientific research are always openly presented, and scientists are honored when their work is published successfully. The details of technological innovations, in contrast, are mostly kept secret, as they bring military and economic benefit to governments and corporations. When all technological developments are freely made open, they cannot be used secretly for evil, and safe and peaceful days will follow.

3. What is Expected of Technology

Technology for nature conservation

People cannot keep their present lifestyles if they want to continue to prosper on Earth. Farming, developed at the end of the Neolithic Era, is far from adequate to provide resources for a human population that will eventually reach 10 billion. In addition, people used to a luxurious lifestyle require even more resources. The planet's resources are limited, and the day will come, in a not-too-distant future, when they are exhausted.

Therefore, there are high expectations that technological development will create environments that are attuned to nature while also facilitating the mass supply of resources. "Development" reminds us instantly of deforestation, dam construction, and residential land development. Such types of development are necessary for humans to live safely and comfortably. Is it permissible, though, to have the kind of development that will destroy a comfortable life in the future for the sake of a comfortable life today? There is nothing flamboyant about the technology of Leigh Creek—introduced below—but it makes comfort possible both now and in the future. Is it not this kind of technology that we should look to? Take a golf course as a familiar example: maintaining the turf by spraying enormous quantities of chemicals such as pesticides is, for the sake of present convenience, destroying the environment that must be maintained into the future. How can we make greens without overusing chemicals in Japan? We should consider how to make golf courses that are suited to the Japanese climate and soils. We should aim to grow the right kind of turfgrass and to establish methods for cultivating it. These things are not impossible. We are simply not keen on training people or developing technologies for these purposes. Maybe we are not so keen because such things are not at all lucrative. —Or do we tell ourselves that we cannot think about the future as we stand and watch the inevitable environmental degradation of this planet?

We must develop technologies that can create environments that are in tune with nature and that can repair the damage to the environment. This is done only haphazardly now, and often only emotionally. The surface of Earth has holes of considerable size, made up of sites that have been devastated and sacrificed to land development for the sake of present convenience alone. The spherophylon living on Earth is not healthy. If we leave it unattended without trying to cure it, the disease might become impossible to cure—and then it will be too late. Therefore, we should urgently develop technologies to diagnose the harm we have done to the environment and to repair it. And we expect to have an increase in engineers who can deal with such matters.

I visited the downstream Mekong delta region in Vietnam in the 1990s. There were expansive mangrove forests, which were simple vegetation just like cultivated cedar forests in Japan. The vegetation in the Mekong delta region was completely annihilated by the defoliation operation during the Vietnam War; the fear of guerillas led the US military to create bare land so they could see in all directions. Later, trees of the family Rhizophoraceae were planted in the region while the sprayed chemicals still remained in the soil. These trees, now 17 or 18 years old, had all reached the same height. Unlike mangrove forests grown naturally, however, these did not have a variety of undergrowth. The diversity of living things had not return to the region yet. I only found some pioneer species that grew on mangroves tentatively trying to regain life. The Rhizophoraceae were almost tall enough to be harvested, but it would take more time for the mangrove forests to regain their nature there. Comparatively simple vegetation like mangroves comes back rather quickly, however, and now it is reported that seemingly natural vegetation can be found in most of the Mekong delta region.

Developing the technology to secure resources is also important. It is essential to secure sufficient resources to prevent starvation and the spread of disease. Preparations are certainly underway for outstanding biotechnology developments, and we may have no need to worry about not having enough young and promising researchers and engineers to engage in the research. Biodiversity research, however, does not garner enough attention yet, though biodiversity is what provides gene pools. People are more interested in developing technologies that seem to be of immediate use, rather than contributing to fundamental science—perhaps out of habit from the days of nationwide efforts to catch up with the modern technology. Needless to say, the refinement of technology is a vital undertaking for the development of human life, but at the same time, if there is not sufficient fundamental research, we may find ourselves short of necessary knowledge when we need it. If we promote only useful science that is needed today, we may become encounter a deficiency of necessary basic scientific knowledge when technology is about to make progress by leaps and bounds. We can find numerous examples of this in history. (On a personal note, it was like this for me: when I started my study of plant systematics, people were derisive, saying it was of no use, and I have long kept up my research like an outsider in the field of biology, but I came to be deeply engaged in the theme of biodiversity in my lifetime, which has vital and urgent significance for society (Iwatsuki, 1997, 2018)).

Learning from nature: what it means to be one with nature
The human race has faced numerous dangers so far and overcome them to attain our present prosperity. We keep trying to make our environment even more comfortable by enhancing technology, in order to overcome the crisis we currently face. Such actions, though, sometimes bring on new problems.

Here is one example. We may cut down hills to create residential land, seeking a comfortable living environment. We then might build a dam upstream to protect the newly created community. The dam itself may harm the river's natural functions, or it could collapse due to torrential rain. In a situation like that, people say, "This was not preventable, as this natural phenomenon was unexpected." Disasters occur often in newly developed areas, and communities that people have lived in for a long time are disaster-resistant. (Here, I would say this would amount to more than centuries, not a few decades.) Are we constructing large-scale residential developments on the premise that devastating damage from natural disasters that occur every several years is permissible? If so, people's lives are considered very cheap. How much progress have we made for people's happiness compared with the primitive era at this rate?

Terraced fields built on the hillside present beautiful scenery, but they are the result of flagrant destruction of nature. In such arable land, however, natural disasters occur rarely. It is slopes that are not under regular maintenance, or newly and forcibly developed areas, that are likely to have disaster risk.

This is something that I experienced in Yunnan Province, China, in the 1990s. In some places, newly built motorways are destroyed by localized torrential downpours every year (color plate). The kind of torrential rain that comes once every few years can damage roads. I was unable to drive to my destinations on some occasions. It was not for me to learn of a road blockade only when I was already in the vicinity, though I always checked the accessibility of the route beforehand. We only had to find a substitute site for our research, but this situation must be extremely inconvenient for residents, whose lives are negatively affected by the shutdown of the traffic network. Which can we depend on safely: the technology to build terraced fields manually, or the technology to build modern roads? Probably no one would say that China is lagging behind in technology. And in technologically advanced Japan, we must not forget cases where we lost many lives due to overconfidence in technology.

Accidents are not just events that are so severe that they cause fatalities. The fact that disasters occur in such visible ways suggests that invisible threats are growing every day. I am not trying to instigate fear idly. We should give more serious consideration to residual chemicals in golf courses, for example. Hormone-disrupting chemicals, though they are finally being viewed as an issue, were practically non-existent for us until quite recently. Such things have been an ongoing cause of harm, whether or not we are aware of it.

How much do we know about nature when we have modified it so much? "Eco-friendly development" is a slogan long in use. What it means, in reality, is often planting nonnative species, for which methods of mass propagation are established, on deforested land that is developed for economic benefit more than anything else. Can we call this eco-friendly development of residential land? The adjective sounds hollow. Do they really believe in this misnomer because they are ignorant about nature? If so, they should learn what their actions signify.

Let us yet again think of our favorite Neolithic Japanese ancestors. They did not possess the knowledge of advanced modern science. Did they not, however, know more about nature than modern people in some ways? They did not submit to nature. They forced considerable modifications on nature with the technologies they obtained. And yet they were children of nature. They lived in harmony with nature. They had real reverence for nature.

It is dangerous to delude ourselves with longing for what we presume to be nature. Humans live as one element of the spherophylon on Earth, playing a part for it (it is a matter of preference whether we value our part as an important). We know this, and we believe that we make sound judgments about our actions. If this is the case, we should regard our individual lives as the life of the spherophylon, and take it as our guiding principle to sustain it for the future. If that is not possible for us, we should stop rebelling against nature and start obeying it. Being one with nature means aiming for harmonious coexistence between nature and people, rather than subjugating nature to people's will, or placing topmost priority on nature in every single act of ours. If we cannot achieve this, Earth's spherophylon cannot hope to survive—and neither can the human race.

I would like to present the following three examples as trials of technology expected to bring about environmental improvement.

Example 1: The development of agriculture in a desert area (Taklamakan Desert)

When I had the opportunity to visit the Taklamakan Desert in Xinjiang-Uygur Autonomous Region, China, I gained a considerable insight from the plants there (Iwatsuki, 1998). As I looked at those halophilous and xerophilous plants in the desert, I was amazed by how freely they lived, going beyond the explanations in ordinary botany textbooks. They helped me realize that human technology could create stable production bases in a supposedly barren land like this.

Plants are not supposed to grow in dry land or saline soil. I will not go into explanations of osmotic pressure of cellular membranes here, but they simply cannot grow due to the physiological principles of the plant cells. In reality, however, plants do grow in dry, saline land. They do not care a fig about what botanical textbooks say. So I wondered if we could identify the genes that enabled the plants to tolerate salinity and drought and incorporate them into other species to create salt-tolerant or drought-resistant rice plants and wheat. If this were possible, the desert would be a rich land of production that could be easily afforested. I did some research and found out that experiments on genetic engineering of this sort was already underway on rice plants, succeeding in creating new strains that were salt- and drought-tolerant to some extent. We know the functions of many of the genes of plants, which makes it easy to experiment on them, as it is easy to assess what genetic modifications would cause what change. Likewise, if we acquire basic knowledge about other plants, this kind of experiment may make considerable progress (as I have often stated, development of state-of-the-art technology requires fundamental information on the species to be experimented on).

Of course, we must give careful consideration on how we use the technology. First, deserts are in themselves one form that the planet's nature takes. Desert greening is an action that will modify that nature—thus destroying nature. We need to conscientiously consider and predict possible repercussions and take preventive measures so that the modifications do not cause disasters. Second, we must note that, although the preliminary experiment on rice plants mentioned earlier succeeded in creating new salt- and drought-tolerant strains, the cellular mechanism that makes this possible has not been identified. It is still at the level where we have managed to breed resistant plants by trial and error, but we are not clear on how. We must have a clear understanding of the current level of technology. This leads to the fact that we cannot eliminate all the risks. Therefore, we must be circumspect in our use of technology. Rather than starting with mass production, we need to conduct repeated preliminary experiments and start with small-scale growing tests. On the other hand, it is also problematic to reject experiments wholesale because safety is not guaranteed 100 percent. That is, we must not lunge ahead recklessly, but we must make careful, steady progress.

Greening is not going well in regions that have turned into desert as a result of human activity. Deforestation accelerates the increase of carbon dioxide. Most greening efforts are done manually by traditional methods, as not much consideration has yet been given to the development of greening technology. Although it is basic technology aimed at improving the habitability of the planet, we do not make proper efforts to bolster it. It is not impossible to maintain and develop even the Taklamakan Desert into a form of nature that continues to coexist harmoniously with people. That is the depth of possibility that our future holds. This applies, however, only if we keep pursuing such possibilities from a long-term perspective. We very much need to develop excellent technologies much further and make use of them for urgent and important issues.

Example 2: Wisdom in terraced fields (Yunnan)

In the olden days, humans chose to inhabit locations in nature that had the most stable conditions for building a settlement. Let us take a look at the region in China that is famously lauded for "plowing into heaven." The hillsides are neatly developed into arable land; well-watered areas are made into paddy fields, while those that are not become vegetable fields, each with suitable crops planted. It is not at all uncommon to find more than 1,000 meters of difference in elevation. Residential areas are often built in well-watered high land that is not prone to landslides and rich in vegetation.

In the morning, people would get up at dawn and breezily walk to the field, not minding the elevation difference of 1,000 meters. In the late afternoon, they would travel back home to high land, as if walking towards the sky that was lighting up with stars. How many hours would this simple commute take?

You may think it is a tough life to walk such a path. As we drove the winding road on the slope, we often met villagers walking by agilely, every time we crossed the path that almost directly ran up to the top. The path was nothing more than an easy walk for them, though. It must be common for families to chat on the way home, going up this path after a day's work.

Which is easier, for them to commute thus, or for you to commute by modern public transport like trains and cars in an urban area? You spend an hour, an hour and a half, or even two hours to get to school or the office in the Tokyo metropolitan area, stuffed in an over-crammed train, keeping a lookout for any sign of a seat becoming available. (I have been doing a 1.5 hour commute each way in the Tokyo metropolitan area while I have been employed.) You often get home after nine or ten, if you do a bit of overtime. You may even miss the last train if you have a few drinks with your colleagues. There cannot be many families that have dinner together. You can have meat or fish with beer or wine for dinner, but all these are standard supermarket fare. The height of civilization, you may say sarcastically. After the evening meal, some people may go to gym, spending their hard-earned money to cope with a lack of exercise. Burdened with over-nutrition and obesity, they see a doctor and try hard to slim down.

The Yunnan families have a meager meal of a few dishes and one bowl of soup after climbing up 1,000 meters without breaking a sweat, but they enjoy the evening meal together. What they have for dinner is food that they harvest themselves. The cooking might be a little salty one day, and a little too thin on another, but they enjoy each unique flavor by adding salt or water at the dinner table. The big boy might be clouted by the father if he helps himself to a large portion of food. The younger child might start crying, watching that scene. The dinner table is never quiet; it is buzzing with life.

Many people would not be able to give a quick answer if asked which lifestyle they would choose. Those who are accustomed to the urban life cannot bear a life without neon lights for long. That is fine. It is one choice to prefer the world of comforts that civilization offers (no need to derogatively call it "contaminated by civilization"). Yet, if that is our choice, shouldn't we be more eager to realize the ideal of civilization? If we are tormented by the ordeal of commuting, we should foster an environment that mitigates the pain.

Example 3: A green city in the desert (Leigh Creek)

There is a coal-mining town in South Australia called Leigh Creek. It is about 700 kilometers north of (or inland from) Adelaide, the capital of South Australia—that is to say, right in the middle of desert. I visited the city in 1989 to observe a greening project there.

To commemorate the 200th anniversary of the nation's founding, South Australia built a large-scale tropical greenhouse at the Adelaide Botanic Garden, with the purpose of creating a research base for conservation of genetic resources in the tropics and arid areas. On that occasion I visited the city of Adelaide, and my itinerary included a visit to the arid region. Deserts and other types of dry land entranced me, as I was used to doing research in the humid tropics.

Though prosperous in nineteenth century, Port Augusta became gradually uninhabitable as rainfall levels dropped. One of the town's development projects was to build an arid-land botanical garden, in collaboration with Adelaide Botanic Gardens. The botanical garden was also supposed to conduct research on the greening of arid zone. I was taken to the plot of land where the garden was going to be built; it was a wide-open space in a semi-desert area, with just acacia shrubs growing there.

A two-lane road ran almost directly north from Port Augusta. There was nothing in the desert aside from the road. We sometimes saw emus standing still, and when we took a break once, a surprised kangaroo jumped out from behind a eucalyptus tree. We passed by a sightseeing spot on the way: a house deserted by settlers who left it when the reduced rainfall made it uninhabitable. Reading the plaque for the ruin, Dr. John Simmons, then the curator of the Royal Botanic Gardens at Kew, mumbled that the house had been built in the same year as his own.

Leigh Creek was first built to mine the fine coal it produces. Its population was 15,000 when we visited. As it was hundreds of kilometers away from neighboring towns, Leigh Creek needed to be able to sustain its residents' lives on its own. For that, greening was eagerly awaited, even more so because the town was in the arid region. That was the premise of Leigh Creek's town planning.

South Australia is advanced in researching the greening of dry land, as it contains large expanses of arid lands. Leigh Creek also has a greening research institute, which conducts research on selecting plants suitable for the town and finding out how much irrigation is needed for each plant in each season to sustain its life with the minimum amount of water. Based on that data, selected and propagated seedlings are given away to residents, along with irrigation manuals. People help with greening by following the manuals, for the purpose of creating the environment for themselves. Fostered thus, the trees lining the streets and the garden plants help create a town pretty rich in greenery in the middle of the arid land.

I suggested bringing water in through pipes, using the money earned from coal mining, but they explained to me problems unknown to someone like me who is from a mountainous country. Precipitation is far outweighed by transpiration in the arid lands in semi-deserts. If you continue to irrigate the land in such a region, the excess water mostly transpires. You cannot expect water to be absorbed into green-covered soil and the excess to flow down to a river, as in Japan. What happens if a large amount of transpiration continues to occur? Induced by transpiration, salt will be drawn up from underground, and in no time will accumulate on the surface, making it saline, which is far worse than dry soil; it will be barren unless a great deal of care is taken to make it arable. Saline soil is a troublesome problem in desert regions.

Some suggest that the people of Leigh Creek need not worry about a distant future, because a coal mining town should only function for a limited period of time, as coal is a limited resource. When I put this argument to them, they reminded me of the ruin that we had seen on the way. It used to be an inhabitable place, but it became barren due to a climate change that had occurred in such a short span of time that we were able to witness it in our lifetime. Conversely, no one can deny the possibility that even an arid land like Leigh Creek, where people can only live in an artificially built town, may become a rainy land suitable for human habitation in a century, five centuries, or ten centuries. If that happened, and yet the land was saline, what would our descendants say of the people that made it infertile? We should not do something that makes our descendants ashamed of us, they say. They explained to me that it was a matter of what kind of town they wanted to build, which made perfect sense.

As it was a town of 15,000 people, it had some amusement centers, but outdoor sports were also necessary. They had a golf course, though it was a nine-hole course, as is often the case in Australia. Visiting the town in the dry season, we were amazed to see the golf course (color plate). The green, at least, was irrigated and had some turf, but the fairway had only some trimmed acacia shrubs. Players must often have a hard time trying to get the golf ball out of the shrubs. "What a tough course," I thought aloud. My guide gave a wry smile and said, "But those playing in a tournament here are all equally disadvantaged."

Recently, I asked for a photograph of that golf course so that I could show it in my public lectures. I was going to use it as an example of people playing golf in adverse conditions. On the contrary, they sent me back a slide of a beautiful golf course covered in green, even on some parts of the fairway. As they were so committed to turning the arid lands green, they must have felt the urge to let me know, as the visitor from a country of lush green, that they were making such success already.

4. Creating an Environment that Transcends Time and Space

The development and creation of the environment

The development of terrace fields that "lead up to heaven" is also a typical example of destroying nature. Rural villages that seem to be surrounded by rich nature are of course the result of agricultural land conversion, and the beautiful flower gardens in alpine countries are the product of farmland conversion: both are the result of the destruction of nature. Land development that makes full use of technology, by definition, causes destruction to nature. Therefore, even creating an environment, which will be discussed here, must be called one form of destruction of nature. Even so, it is pointless to categorically define any act that has an impact on nature as the destruction of nature. We need to have a clear recognition that some acts that are viewed this way are desirable, while others are needless and dangerous.

People developed the environment of the planet for the sake of their own prosperity. When they did not have much power, the development of the environment progressed in harmony with the planet. The headlong development of technology, however, came to put more stress on the planet than people intended. If we conduct land development only for our immediate gain, it will induce degradation of the environment and threaten the survival of the spherophylon. We should eliminate such destructive actions, as they are pointless and dangerous.

What kind of development is actually desirable in spite of being defined as destruction of nature? This should be planned from the perspective of creating an environment that values the life of Earth's spherophylon, which transcends time and space. This means that the environment that we plan to create must also transcend time and space. Land development that only pursues short-term benefits without giving any consideration to its future repercussions presents the risk of someday causing serious harm to the life of the spherophylon; it is not permissible as an approach for environmental creation. Life dwells in cells, in individuals, and in the spherophylon. Therefore, environmental creation needs to consider the entire spherophylon, not just the interests of individuals.

What is required of us in creating an environment is the wisdom to balance the pursuit of people's present wealth with the eternal life of the spherophylon; in other words, to make our coexistence with nature as harmonious as possible. The world's population is rising steadily, placing more demands on resources. The finite resources of the planet will be exhausted one day, if we only use those that exist in nature. This means that we are sacrificing the future for the sake of today. We therefore need to curb population growth while promoting stable supply of resources—but we do not see that happening. Sustainable use of biodiversity is also so often talked about; this is about coordinating conservation with development and use, an idea that should be acceptable to most people. When it comes to how this can be managed in reality, however, it is not so plainly to see, and hardly any effort is put into achieving it because people value immediate economic efficiency more.

The sustainable use of biodiversity may include devising new plants that influence the environment. Just as we have cultivated domesticated plants for food, we should make urgent efforts to create plants that shape the environment and propagate them. We should grow plants that are suited to dry land and saline soil like deserts, for example. In fact, there are plants that grow in arid and saline land. We should borrow the traits that make it possible for those plants to live in such environments and lend them to others. Living in harmony with nature should conform to plants' way of living as a rule, but it is also an option to modify plants so they can adapt to the environment. Humankind has made great achievements in cultivating beautiful plants and increasing their yield. Now it should also be our goal to grow sturdy plants; it is about time we had some scientific development to create new technology.

Creating an environment that transcends time

What is involved in creating an environment that protects the spherophylon on Earth, which transcends time? The answer is quite simple. It is creating an environment that is intended to keep the planet as a whole alive for ever. We must adopt this perspective clearly.

From this standpoint, it is obvious how shameful it is to develop the environment only for the purpose of one's own immediate benefit. Our Neolithic ancestors who built the foundation of prosperity for humanity over the succeeding 25 centuries managed, without having any theory, to create an environment that helped the planet's spherophylon flourish beyond time and space. Modern people have built civilizations on the back of such prosperity. We owe so much to our forebears—what are we doing for the human race in the future? Are we succeeding in developing a planet that we could proudly present to our descendants?

I explained the city planning of Leigh Creek in the previous section. This scheme is not lucrative for anyone, as it does not attempt large-scale construction. It is destroying nature without a doubt, since it is an attempt to turn a desert into a green area. Yet this can be called a typical example of environmental creation that transcends time and space that is within our reach now.

The living environment that people build in deserts is quite impressive. Attempts by residents at harmonious coexistence with nature in such regions, where biodiversity is extremely low, offer rich insight to those of us in Japan, where biodiversity is nearly as high as that in the humid tropics.

How people live on Earth today is one result of having lived through the history of evolution that spans over more than three billion years. And today is the starting point of a life that will go on for billions of years more. We should have that in mind when we plan on environmental creation.

186

Creating an environment that transcends space

Things are now progressing on a global scale. Excess emissions of carbon dioxide are suspected of causing climate change, including global warming as well as various frequent natural disasters throughout the world. As for global warming, it is not a hazard that can be prevented by the efforts of one person, one company, or one nation. Earth is one planet. This is no time to be pursuing the benefits of nations or individuals only.

The Mekong is one of the largest rivers in the world, running through the Indochinese Peninsula. When I visited Laos in 1990s, the Mekong was flooding, as it was an exceptionally rainy year. I had heard that a massive dam, built on the Nam Ngum with the assistance of overseas aid from Japan, had gotten the almost annual flooding under control, and its hydroelectric power generation was producing tremendous loads, most of which were being exported to Thailand, becoming a valuable source of foreign currency for the nation.

That year, however, the country was experiencing flooding for the first time in some years. (We had to take a detour, spending extra hours to get to our destination.) They had flood control in place that would have withstood abnormal rainfall to some extent. That year, however, the precipitation was not only extraordinary, but it rose unusually fast.

The Mekong River originates in Qinghai Province and passes through Yunnan Province, China. People in Laos and Thailand presumed that the unheard-of rapid increase in the water level must have been caused by some occurrence in Yunnan Province, like some change in the forests there. This surmise was not based on proper research, but if this was true, nothing could be done to prevent flooding in Laos and Thailand, except fortifying embankments at the most. What would happen if they built the embankments on the main stem higher? The Nam Ngum and other big rivers in Laos are all tributaries of the Mekong River. This means that the water of the main stem river flows back into them ruthlessly. Therefore, fortifying the embankments is no easy feat. When flooding happens in Japan, embankments are breached locally, and the river water floods the places it flows to. In the Mekong River, the back currents flood into the plains and remain there, forming ponds, since the land is lower than the water level of the river. (I was horrified to see a great flood when I was still in college; the Yodo River was overflowing into the reclaimed land that was formerly Ogura Pond in Kyoto in the 1950s. Still, the flood subsided in a week or so.) Floods in Laos and Northern Thailand are on a different scale; the plains, as far as you can see, are all flooded, and you have no clue when the water level of the river might go down and the floods subside. Even detecting the cause of floods is a major international affair; making flood prevention plans, even more so. This reminds me: didn't relevant nations discuss a comprehensive development plan for the Mekong River for many years, without coming up anything concrete?

The lesson we can learn from the Mekong River floods is that the life of the planet's spherophylon does not dwell in localized areas, and so constructive actions to preserve it cannot even begin if we are bound by arbitrary national borders set down by people. Environmental creation for the sake of the spherophylon must transcend territory. Its life does not take place in a limited space. Instead of trying to confine it in a set space, we should think of its movement into the future. Surely it is not necessary to mention that environmental issues such as global warming, acid rain, and endocrine disrupters take place on a global scale: all of them require a mindset and actions that transcend space.

5. Human Life and the Spherophylon

Loving the spherophylon on Earth

The spherophylon expands globally in both time and in space. If we consider Earth to be one component of the universe, we can call it a being that lives in the universe.

The accumulated time amounting to four billion years (which may be nothing unusual in astronomy and geology, but is an extremely large figure in our daily life) makes us deeply aware of the weight of history, and how precious it is, when we think about the life of the spherophylon. Life has continued all through those years up to today, without a moment of interruption. That life is entrusted to each of us living things.

Reverence for life is also reverence for the mystery hidden inside us. Our lives have a history of over three billion years. The lives of cockroaches and earthworms also have the history of the same length. The life of a colon bacillus happens to dwell in a colon bacillus today, but it could have easily been in a rice plant that produces rice, a cow that produces beef, or in you. It so happens that there is a life in the form of a colon bacillus, and there is another in your form, and all together they form a single system.

Even if someone told you to love all living things because we are all creatures living on Earth, you would still dislike those that you dislike, and you would not be able to love those that had nothing to do with you in your life. So I would not ask that of you. Rather, I ask you if you can still eliminate those that you dislike while knowing that our relationships with all the living things on Earth are relationships between individual components of a single life called a spherophylon—a community of lives sharing a common destiny. People would not cut off their noses if they disliked the shape of them (though some seem to torment themselves by resorting to the wrong kind of technology to shape them to suit their fancy). Would you say that the brain and the stomach were important, but you could do without your legs because they are not shapely? Skin cells, which you shed every day thanks to your metabolism, are important tissues that make up the body, without which your life is not complete. Although the individual cells that make up the body are living independently to some extent, people cannot exist without skin. You as an individual are formed only when trillions of cells come together, and only when you live as an individual can your brain and stomach function properly. Furthermore, there is so much that we do not know even about ourselves, much less about the life of the spherophylon. How much of its knowledge has science uncovered, and how much do you know about it? Given all this, how should you act toward it?

People dislike what they dislike. Even if we are told to cherish creatures living in nature, it is hard to force ourselves to like them by the power of reasoning. It takes a radical reform in how we regard them. It may be only natural for us to decide if we like something or not at a first glance. There are people who are passionate about some sports clubs, but such aficionados actually do not have any concrete reasons for their passion. They just like their team and dislike others for inexplicable reasons. If they feel passionate about it, their feelings become even fiercer, and no one can force them to change. When it comes to creatures living on Earth, it may be all right to simply like or dislike them by instinct, but we must not forget at the same time that they share a fate with us, beyond time and space. If we become aware of that aspect, perhaps we can begin to see them in ways beyond simple liking and disliking. When our new regard for them deepens, it may grow into affection for creatures of this world, which are, just like us, individual components of the spherophylon.

We saw so much wildlife in the countryside where I grew up. Though I was frail, I caught so many insects, killed them, and pulled out wild plants. As I had fun tumbling around in the field, I gradually came to feel that things in nature were my precious friends. Contact fosters love. Those creatures are my fellows in forming the single spherophylon that I should regard as myself. The feeling I have for myself should directly translate to the feeling I have for them. Those who had the experience of observing nature should always remember this. People should have more interactions with creatures around them and have fun with them from this perspective, just as you live every day with the body that forms the individual that is you.

Either in harmony with nature or conquering nature

Creatures in general lead lives adapted to the planet's environment. Those that cannot do so go extinct. Thus, their way of living becomes attuned to the planet. Humans, as one of the species of living things, lived in harmony with the planet through trial and error, but people preferred to conquer the planet, confident in their technology. This trend is particularly conspicuous in people who brandish.

Probably because the terrain was simple, the plains in Europe were thoroughly developed until farms and ranches accounted for most of the land. Lush greenery was increasingly developed into farmland in the US as well. Before we knew it, many species were extinct or on the verge of extinction, which significantly lowered biodiversity. We courted doom for the future, while we thought we were conquering nature and building our civilization.

Fortunately, Japan was blessed with an abundance of nature until quite recently, and maintained a forest coverage rate of over 80 percent, partly due to its rugged terrain. People lived in harmony with nature until after the Edo period (that is, for some 260 peaceful years from the seventeenth through the nineteenth centuries). After the Meiji Restoration in 1868, which initiated the era of modernization for Japan, people followed the example of Western countries in everything, including attempts to conquer nature. The nation's prosperity after World War II accelerated that trend to the extreme. As a result, the number of endangered species rose greatly in Japan, too.

Western countries and Japan did become earnestly engaged in domestic efforts to conserve nature, but destruction nonetheless spread to the entire planet, accelerating the speed of species extinction. We have greatly damaged the life of the spherophylon, and played a part in driving it into illness. Furthermore, we are not aware of that fact, or we have become used to pretending ignorance even if we are.

Conquering nature sounds grand. If that were really possible, it would be one option for us. In reality, however, I believe we have convinced ourselves that conquering nature means exploiting it. Should this be allowed to continue? Humans were originally a product of nature. What would happen if creatures stopped living with their mother, the planet? What consequences would there be if living things, instead of adapting to the planet, only abused it at will? Without fully understanding the planet, and brandishing tremendous power with underdeveloped technology while having no clue about the consequences, at that. Some have likened this situation to an infant brandishing a pistol, but it may be more like giving an infant the nuclear button, considering the dearth of our knowledge and the power of technology that we use.

No one cuts flesh off their own body for profit. What some of us are doing to Earth now is the same as cutting flesh off the spherophylon and harming its eternal life. People who cannot feel pain will gradually drive themselves to death, never realizing the wound they made. We know how deeply ailing our spherophylon is on Earth, from various facts. We know how it is hurting. The least we can do, then, is to take care of ourselves and devotedly protect our life—and by "our" I mean the spherophylon's. That is what it means to cherish the life of the spherophylon that lives on Earth, transcending time and space.

People living in harmony with nature

Constructing highly advanced civilizations, humans evolved into people, uniquely different from other creatures: a being opposed to nature of the planet. There is no point in debating the right or wrong of this, since we cannot turn back history once it has been carved in stone. What we can do, however, is have an accurate understanding of the reality that we face, live through it and build the future.

It is not yet possible to demonstrate scientifically and empirically what the guiding principles are for evolution in nature. An error in the transcription of a DNA base sequence creates a new gene structure; when the error is repeated and selected, it leads to the formation of a new species. The accumulated changes recorded over a long history become the historical process called evolution, bringing about diverse forms of life on Earth. Evolution can be traced as historical fact only within a certain range. No matter how much of the history of evolution science uncovers, creatures continue to age, beyond their three billion years of history. In all this, the position of the species called humans has become a curious thing; the part of the spherophylon called humans has become rebellious against the spherophylon in the aggregate. It has even started trying to determine the future of the spherophylon.

Rebellious acts against natural change, or human acts—artificiality against nature, in other words—cannot be categorically labelled as evil. If natural development is transcendentally defined as good, going against it is evil, but what happens in nature is in itself natural, beyond good or evil. Defiance of nature thus cannot be judged good or evil, either. There may be good rebellion and evil rebellion. Defiance in itself may not be either good or evil, but the actions may bring good results or end in bad ones. Therefore, those who consciously carry out rebellious acts must calculate beforehand whether their acts will result in good or bad. The assessment of the acts may vary, according to the perspective: whether it is good or bad for the individual who does the act, for the human race, or for the spherophylon. Yet we can be sure about one thing: good that transcends time and space for the spherophylon eventually brings good to humans, or the individual, and any act that contains evil repercussions for the spherophylon will ultimately prove detrimental to the survival of humankind; furthermore, it does not guarantee the survival of the individual who carried out the act.

Individuals are the agents of actions, but they only see immediate losses and gains. They are only conscious of creature comforts to survive this moment. They think they can afford to care about their survival tomorrow only after managing to live through today. There is a wide range of choices, however, between choosing a hard but wise way to transcend time and space in order to survive today, or electing to take an easy and wasteful option without giving consideration on the future generation's doom. The choice is now left, to a great extent, to the agent of actions—people. The future of the spherophylon on Earth is up to the choices we make in our actions.

The survival of the transcendent life of the spherophylon on Earth depends on how harmoniously we manage to live with nature. If we seek to preserve the life of the spherophylon on this planet—that is to say, if we mean to conserve the species of the human race—we need to succeed in creating harmonious coexistence with nature of the planet Earth.

CHAPTER
8

❄

WHAT WE ARE TO CREATE

Environmental creation based on people's wishes

The human environment is not for specific people, but for everyone living on Earth. But does all humanity share this idea? Even if people do believe it, isn't it the case that they just have this vague idea that someone will take care of it for them? People do not seem to care themselves. The matter of the human environment, however, cannot be evaluated in this moment alone, but needs to be thought through from a perspective that transcends time and space. (This is to say that the human environment is also that of the spherophylon, which transcends time and space while it lives.) The worst is not thinking about it. When you are loaded down with daily care, you cannot afford to worry about tomorrow. So you leave it to others to worry about it, perhaps.

This would be fine if leaving it to others worked. The truth is that we have been driven into a situation where it is hard to hope for a bright future for this planet. We may soon reach the point of no return. Would those unconcerned people still say that it did not matter because they would not witness the end of Earth?

It is not that everyone can equally and creatively contribute to the future of the human environment. Scientists must have an accurate understanding of what is happening to the planet, and have probable predictions about its future. Engineers must build more advanced technology and use it properly to contribute to the prosperity of human life. Policymakers must evaluate policies to survive today the best way we can, and make decisions on what needs to be done and what must not be done, to make the planet's environment inhabitable for people a century, or ten centuries from now. Other people must have other things they should take responsibility for in their own fields of expertise. If they all did their jobs in the best way, the general public would only need to lead everyday life under the guidance of these specialists.

In reality, the strain on the environment is becoming worse as we are preoccupied with our daily business. Who is to blame? Rather than trying to find the culprit, let us think about who will suffer the consequences. Can this planet, the wealth accumulated in history, be allowed to be exhausted for temporary pleasure? Our planet is not just for us, but also for our children and grandchildren. Should we live today leaving problems for future generations? The environment must be treated properly if we want to maintain this planet for the sake of our descendants, too. Our Neolithic ancestors devised a splendid policy for the sustainable use of the planet. Modern people, with our advanced civilization, cannot fail to do better than they did. We have to be prepared to have the lifestyles that we enjoy today restricted and suffer inconveniences in various aspects of life. Ants, which know the hardships of winter, also know to enjoy their labors in summer. Humans, who call themselves the Lords of Creation, surely must be able to do what ants can do. It must be done for the sake of the life of the spherophylon that is us—and ultimately for the individual that is you.

We must face the reality of our situation. If we can safely lead a life of pleasure, let us enjoy it by all means. Environmental issues, however, are not just something that scientists, engineers, corporate managers, and policymakers all have to engage in with their own power, which goes without saying; they are also something that every one of us must become aware of and take action on, or they will not be acted upon definitively. All the people must have a correct understanding of where the problems lie, and decide whether leaders are making the right decisions. If there is a need to restrict people's pleasure in life, all people must think over it particularly carefully. (During the COVID-19 pandemic, most people wore a mask, stayed at home whenever it was necessary, and got vaccinated as soon as possible, even though they did not like doing so.) It is a fantasy to believe that a limited number of leaders will be able to guide people in the right direction over a matter that everyone should be dealing with. Such a matter can be solved only when everyone takes the initiative acting upon the consensus of the people. If environmental creation does not become something that all people wish for, the creation of an environment that enables us to use the planet sustainably will end up being up a dream of oddballs. Humankind in the next generation will lose its habitat on Earth, and will go into eternal exile or follow the path to its doom. If that is the current consensus, it certainly is our choice. I wonder whether I will end up being among the minority in that case.

Everyone should know

Nowadays, people think too lightly of the planet and biodiversity. It may be because our habitat is in such a comfortable condition right now, but we are extremely optimistic about the future of the spherophylon on Earth. If we can survive with this mindset, there's no need to say anything about it. There are, however, only very limited occasions to learn about the reality of biodiversity.

While science and technology are advanced, social education and life-long learning on science have fallen far behind. We have good museums and other facilities, and their contents are becoming richer. Yet, we hardly have any institutions concerned with biodiversity, which is often pointed out by my colleagues. It is partly the fault of researchers in this field, including me. I do accept the blame where it is due, but still worry that we will be very sorry in the near future—say, 10 or 20 years down the line—if we do not take constructive action immediately. I cannot help but warn that we urgently need to establish an institution that collects information on biodiversity, build services that make it available to the general public, and proactively educate people on the significance of the sustainable use of biodiversity. As noted in chapter 6, GBIF was established and fairly a good amount of data has been accessed by now, though I am sad to say that this organization is not developing very much compared that it was expected.

Relevant research institutes must be run by creative researchers who further untangle the reality of biodiversity and build on this scientific discipline. As I have mentioned, concrete plans for such schemes have already been proposed in Japan—BoSSCo and GaiaList, for example. A proposal to found a national museum of natural history in Ryukyu is said to be under positive consideration by the decision makers concerned. By establishing such institutions and collecting basic data on biodiversity that is missing now, I hope that all the people on Earth will be able to learn and think about the global issues we are facing, as well as the predicted and the ideal future of the planet, and will take action to create the future. If, even after that, the consensus of people on Earth is to allow the human race to go extinct, I may have nothing to say against it. As it is now, however, it is as if we are digging our own grave blindfolded, choosing small comforts out of fear of hurting even a little right now. I cannot just sit and watch this happen.

Chopsticks culture and the creation of eternal environment

While Western people may treasure the silver spoons bequeathed to them by their grandparents, and lay them out at the dinner table when they have important guests, Japanese people consider it a luxury to serve guests at the dinner table with chopsticks made of straight-grained cedar wood. Japanese people find the height of luxury in consumable goods— we serve our guests with delicately made chopsticks that will be thrown away after just one use. This is also the difference between the wisdom of living in a few-centuries-old stone houses that has been repaired carefully and the preference for living in wooden houses that can be easily torn down and rebuilt. European people had to conserve nature in order to survive, as they began living aggressively toward nature from early on. They lived in houses made of stones and mud, and polished utensils such as knives and forks, for the sake of avoiding mass consumption of scarce plant resources. Until the Edo period that stretched from the beginning of the seventeenth century to the latter half of the nineteenth century, Japan was blessed with beautiful and bountiful nature, and people did not have to worry about exhausting its products. Thus began the culture of luxury in the lavish use of resources. Chopsticks culture, however, came to show signs of breaking down in the Meiji era during the late nineteenth century, when people started to adopt Western culture.

Chopsticks may be said to symbolize the Japanese culture of sumptuous use of expendables. Japan's unique aesthetics were formed and fostered by this. The reason it lasted so long was because people lived, adapting to this country's nature, in our own way. This could not go on unchanged after we switched to a Western lifestyle. We did not leave behind our culture of viewing consumption as a virtue, though. We even quickly build and destroy buildings made of concrete blocks, just as we did with wooden houses. Actually, concrete buildings have to be rebuilt within a century, in contrast with the oldest wooden buildings maintained for more than 14 centuries, as seen at Horyuji temple.

When we consider that human life depends on limited resources, it is blatantly obvious that what can be consumed has a limit. If consumption is for some aesthetic purpose and can be covered by products of nature, it may have some significance. But if it is consumption for the sake of consumption—if it is promoted recklessly in order to revitalize economic activity—that is nothing but a desecration of limited resources.

Among all types of resources, natural products are valued highly, while artificial ones are regarded to be of lower value, probably because people think technology is limited. Yet, if the endlessly growing global population is to consume the planet's finite resources, it is an inevitable and urgent task for people to substitute artificial resources for natural ones. For that reason, it is vital to refine our technology of producing high-quality artificial products. This means that the technology for producing superior products must be among the approaches we consider for dealing with nature. Our Neolithic ancestors succeeded in creating substitutes for natural resources: domesticated plants and animals.

What is the creation of the environment?

The global population will grow at an accelerated rate if we do nothing about it. Therefore, population control is a vital, imminent matter for the survival of the spherophylon on Earth. That, however, is not the theme of this book. We must be prepared for more than a small uptick in global population, at least for the time being. Geo-environmental issues are always global; population growth in South America or Africa will become an issue for Japan, and naturally the opposite is true, as well. People's lives in a particular country are not self-contained within that country. With that in mind, we should consider how we assess the current situation of the planet and how we can conserve the planet for future generations.

As long as people are alive, their minimum requirements are to secure necessary resources and to prepare a living environment. Then we should make sustainable use of Earth, our only home. The need for the sustainable use of biodiversity comes from the same idea.

When the population grows, it naturally requires more resources. Further, if it is inevitable that as human life becomes diversified, there will be certainly even more demand on resources. We must build our future with that as a given. Therefore, we must increase the supply of resources considerably, even if we are able to reduce demand a little by cutting down on wasteful consumption.

We should speak out about creating better living environments. Since humans damaged the surface of the planet decisively, a harmonious coexistence between nature and humankind has become the paramount challenge for civilization. As I have repeatedly noted, to achieve this, we need to assess the current situation accurately and understand that the life of people living on Earth is the life of the spherophylon that transcends time and space. That is the starting point for everything. The present moment should not be judged by this moment alone; the present is one aspect of historical development. There is no present without the past or the future. We should be duly grateful for our cumulative history, and take full responsibility for the future that should expand infinitely. It is a crime against future generations to idly waste away the present without thinking about our planet, which transcends time and space, and the life of the spherophylon that exists on it.

We should make every effort to develop technology that will enable us to live life beyond time and space. It goes without saying that we must urgently try to bring about spectacular progress in science, which is the foundation of technology, in order to achieve this. Creating and sustaining the optimal environment is the most important issue facing modern people, and for the sake of this, a superb technology must be developed by thoughtful people.

Let Earth's spherophylon prosper

People live the life of the spherophylon, just as they live their individual lives. The planet's spherophylon is a being that has lived through a history of more than three billion years and should live through the infinite future, while it also has a solid presence in the here and now. The role of every single one of us, as one component of the spherophylon, as the human race as a whole, or as an individual that belongs to that species, is to embody the meaning of life beyond time and space.

There is no primitive nature left on Earth due to land development since the Neolithic Age. In spite of this, modern people are strongly nature-oriented. That is why more people are urging us to protect what is left of it for the sake of our comfortable life. Creating an environment that is attuned to nature as it exists now—or what remains of it—in order to keep living in tune with nature: that is the future that modern people seek.

Those who are involved in development projects say that they cannot foresee what will happen three years down the line. Time assessment is talked about in the field of international development assistance, but even projects of a few years sometimes require reassessment of project plans in the implementation phase. This is nowhere near "beyond time and space." Development projects themselves are consumables. Isn't this reality terrifying? Development projects should bear fruit that would benefit our descendants, at least if their purpose is to bring people prosperity. Identifying the knowhow should be our present challenge.

Our children and grandchildren should be allowed to take care of their own eras, instead of spending their lives making up for misdeeds of their parents and grandparents. I do not want us to bring on a terrifying future where Earth no longer exists for our descendants. They say it is the era of globalization—the globe is on the move now. We should refrain from pursuing petty gains today only to lose the planet tomorrow. The virtuous spend their lives on deeds that carve their names in history. Humanity of the modern era should revitalize its wisdom so that history will not say that the people of the twenty-first century brought an end to Earth.

Challenges for modern humans: what we should create now
The spherophylon is an entity that lives its life. What I have explored in this book is how to allow it to prosper beyond time and space by living its life as our own. To accomplish this, we must first try to make sustainable use of the planet. The life of the spherophylon is dependent on inorganic matter on Earth. Every one of us should take action in our own position for the sake of our only planet and its spherophylon. No one will give us any good ideas if we wait. Every single one of us, who has carved the history of evolution on Earth, should do what we can do in our power proactively. It is the wish of our spherophylon itself to try to achieve the eternal prosperity of the spherophylon on Earth; it is our role, as its components, to take action.

For that purpose, we require guiding principles that suit everyone. We must grasp the current situation of the planet in order to set them down, since it is not possible to achieve something with nothing but ideals, without knowing facts. Experts in particular fields should, of course, strive to uncover facts in their own fields, but they should also present the facts they find to the general public in a manner that is as easy to understand as possible. It is naturally the responsibility of policymakers to provide the researchers with subsidies for such activities. Everyone living on Earth should exercise their intellectual curiosity voraciously. Those who do not seek gain nothing. If we only wait, we will end up as the ignorant, blindly obedient masses. Surely people must have learned that from experience well enough over the long course of history. Observe what is happening on Earth as accurately and minutely as possible. Seek out information, for our own sake, on what kind of data is needed and what facilities are necessary to access data accurately and with certainty. When you learn what the reality is, you will know what you have to do next.

The planet of the future should be built in a way that allows it to transcend time and space. Even our daily, localized activities affect the future globally in some way. We cannot take responsibility for our actions unless we have a transcendent perspective. We should pursue the joy of ants, rather than the pleasure of grasshoppers. Your actions will probably take a transcendent form if you gain an accurate understanding of the current reality of Earth, in comparison with its ideal future vision. Then, everyone will love the planet, love the nation, love themselves, and love the spherophylon that is living on Earth.

Individuals exist within the whole, as components of the whole. Unless the whole is alive, individuals cannot survive. At the same time, the survival of the whole is not possible unless the individual components are alive. Your happiness, as an individual, is not complete within you alone. How can you, as a component of the spherophylon, be happy if it is not? This moment is not everything. Individual peace today remains transient without transcendent happiness.

Concluding remarks: for the healthy growth of the life of the spherophylon
Everyone hopes to have a healthy and blessed life. This is generally taken to mean one's own individual life, but now it is understood to refer also that of the spherophylon of which everyone is an element. The happy life of each individual person is variously discussed, and I am hesitant to allude to it in this limited space. Further, I am supposed to talk about techniques for ensuring that the spherophylon has a healthy and blessed life.

The fundamental duty for people on Earth is to recognize what that healthy and blessed life is, and how everyone should contribute to create it. The life of the spherophylon is maintained by all of its components, including every person on Earth, and all of the spherophylon's components must give it love. People on Earth generally love themselves, and this must be true for spherophylon as well. Out of all the various components of spherophylon, only people recognize it consciously.

We often forget that the first step to taking action is to grasp the real facts of the matter. We have not learned about the structure and function of the spherophylon in school, and we know little about its life. First of all, therefore, we should learn about the spherophylon. Then, I am sure everyone will love the spherophylon enough to sustain its life on Earth forever. I hope all the people on Earth will be as interested in learning about the life of spherophylon as they are about themselves.

In looking straight on the life of spherophylon, people will recognize the fact that there are a variety of severe imbalances among the seven billion members of humankind currently alive on Earth. In fact, the spherophylon on Earth is suffering an illness at the moment that is particularly caused by imbalance among its components. Everyone wants to recover from an illness afflicting their own body, and this should be applied to the life of the spherophylon, too. People with higher culture, calling themselves the Lords of Creation, will find a way to heal the illness of the spherophylon. Everyone on Earth can maintain at least a peaceful and mundane life, if not a very rich and luxuriant ones. And the technology to sustain the life of the spherophylon is expected to be developed.

Scientists will uncover various unknown facts or shed light on the truth in nature, and technologists will establish novel technologies to develop the human power to improve the lives of people on Earth. Scientists and technologists usually work on their own subjects, and their focus is in finding new facts in their targets. Sometimes, the new facts elucidated by scientists are used to create new technologies that are used in the wrong ways—for instance, in wars. We remember Alfred Nobel's creation of dynamite, which became essential for weapons, and the creation of nuclear power, which has accompanied disasters.

Scientists and technologists in particular are warned to keep a wide scope of vision and to always see the influence of their success, so that the information around their findings and creations may better be disclosed freely in international society.

Policymakers are to get consensus globally, and economic leaders should be responsible for maintaining economic balance throughout the world. For the sake of this, constant disclosure of information is expected in these areas, too.

Maintaining the health of the spherophylon is a global issue for people, and decision makers should be responsible for maintaining it with support of all the people living on Earth. Those who contribute to the growth of the spherophylon should be responsible for its future: scientists, technicians, policymakers, economic leaders, media people, NGO sectors, and so on should be responsible for their own areas. The most important thing is that every person on Earth must carefully observe every movement and fact performed in international society, and everyone on Earth is responsible for maintaining the health of the spherophylon so that it can grow in a happy and blessed way.

"Sustainable development" is a global theme at present. SDGs, Sustainable Development Goals, were proposed in a 2015 UNEP meeting as a guideline to be accomplished during 2016 and 2030. This concept, however, is based on people's viewpoints toward this expression, and people are taking the position that they will use the planet and its components as resources for their own lives. In this relationship, people always expect to aim for profit or loss: they often emphasize today's success only, overlooking all the negative effects that can be introduced by today's activities. People usually believe they will maintain planet based on their knowledge and power, but I am proposing here—learning from the traditional Japanese (almost forgotten by modern Japanese) who established a lifestyle that maintained a harmonious co-existence between nature and humankind—to cherish the life of spherophylon. It seems difficult for the general public to modify their lifestyle in order to realize the sustainable development of our planet, and it may better suggest that they reverse the concept and live the life of a healthy spherophylon. It is easy for everyone on Earth to take care of themselves, as individuals as well as an element of the spherophylon. Finally, loving the spherophylon will bring about the sustainability of our only Earth and of each individual human being.

Acknowledgments

Three respected friends and biologists, the plant taxonomist David Boufford, the developmental biologist Motonori Hoshi, and the geneticist Takeshi Seno, read the manuscript and provided valuable comments. Their generous help occasioned important improvements in the text.

I am grateful to the distinguished biologist and president emeritus of the Missouri Botanical Garden Peter Raven for providing the insightful and thought-provoking Foreword. Dr. Raven takes issue, for instance, with my characterization of population growth as a successful outcome of the development of agriculture. He urges a greater sense of urgency about species extinction, meanwhile, than he perceives in my discussion of biodiversity. Dr. Raven's comments furnish invaluable context, and I encourage the reader to mull them while perusing the material in question.

This book is an adaptation of a work that I published in Japanese in 1999 as *Seimeikei—seibutsu tayosei no atarashii kangae* (Seimeikei: a new concept of biodiversity). Takako Iwaki translated the original Japanese text into English. I subsequently reworked the English text greatly. That included incorporating information that has become available over the quarter century since the original book appeared, as well as reflecting the helpful input noted above.

The work of shaping this adaptation also included thorough and immensely beneficial editing by Katherine Heins. I thank Waku Miller and Taeko Kudo for the design and layout of the book. And we have Shiyu Oura to thank for the compelling artistry on view in figure 5. Most of all, Yukiko Fujimoto has my eternal gratitude for believing in my work and for resolving to share it with the English-speaking world through her publishing boutique, Bookend.

The cash portion of the International Cosmos Prize award that I received in 2016 defrayed part of the production expenses for this book. That is highly appropriate, since the concept discussed on the preceding pages meshes with the prize's orientation. The prize sponsor, the Expo '90 Foundation, has provided valuable assistance in distributing this book.

BIBLIOGRAPHY

Bianconi, Eva, Allison Piovesan, Federica Facchin, Alina Beraudi, Raffaella
    Casadei, Flavia Frabetti, Lorenza Vitale, Maria Chiara Pelleri, Simone
    Tassani, Francesco Piva, Soledad Perez-Amodio, Pierluigi Strippoli, and Silvia
    Canaider. "An Estimation of the Number of Cells in the Human Body." *Annals
    of Human Biology* 40 (July 2013): 463–71.

Domoto, Akiko, Kunio Iwatsuki, Takeo Kawamichi, and Jeffrey A. MacNeely,
    eds. *A Threat to Life: The Impact of Climate Change on Japan's Biodiversity*. Tokyo:
    Tsukiji Shokan, 2000. Originally published in Japanese as *Ondanka ni owareru
    ikimono tachi* (1997).

Gurdon, John B. "Adult Frogs Derived from the Nuclei of Single Somatic Cells."
    Developmental Biology 4 (February 1962): 256–73.

Gurdon, John B. "The Developmental Capacity of Nuclei Taken from Intestinal
    Epithelium Cells of Feeding Tadpoles." *Journal of Embryology and Experimental
    Morphology* 10 (December 1962): 622–40.

Haeckel, Ernst. *Generelle Morphologie der Organismen* [General morphology of
    organisms]. Vol. 1. Berlin: G. Reimer, 1866.

Haeckel, Ernst. *The Riddle of the Universe*. Translated by Joseph McCabe. New
    York and London: Harper & Brothers Publishers, 1901. Originally published
    in German as *Die Welträtsel* (1899).

Hara, Hiroshi, ed. *Origin and Evolution of Diversity in Plants and Plant Communities*.
    Tokyo: Academia Scientific Book, Co., 1985.

Hara, Toshiro. "Tako tai hito" [Octopuses, sea bream, and humans]. *Biohistory*
    9 (September 1995): 11.Iwatsuki, Kunio. *Bunmei ga sodateta shokubutsutachi*
    [Diversification of plants under the impact of civilization]. Tokyo: University
    of Tokyo Press, 1997. Translated in Chinese by Lin Sujuan as *Wenming Yu
    Zhiwu Jinhua* (Kunming: Yunnan Science & Technology Press, 2001).

Iwatsuki, Kunio. *Nachuraru hisutori* [Natural history]. Tokyo: University of Tokyo
    Press, 2018.

Iwatsuki, Kunio. "Plant Systematics in the Twenty-First Century under Social
    Impact: A Case Study of Systematic Botany in Japan." In *Plant Systematics for*

the Twenty-First Century, edited by Bertil Nordenstam, Gamal El-Ghazaly, and Mohamed Kassas, 297–304. London: Portland Press, 1999.

Iwatsuki, Kunio. *Seimeikei—seibutsutayosei no atarashii kangae* [Spherophylon: A new concept of biodiversity]. Tokyo: Iwanami Shoten, Publisher, 1999.

Iwatsuki, Kunio. *Shida shokubutsu no shizenshi* [Natural history of ferns]. Tokyo: University of Tokyo Press, 1997.

Iwatsuki, Kunio. *Shiruku Rodo ni ikiru shokubutsutachi* [Plants growing along the Silk Road]. Kyoto: Kenseisha, 1998.

Iwatsuki, Kunio. "Spherophylon, the Concept of Life at a Level Higher than That of the Individual." *Proceedings of the Japan Academy, Series B* 82 (December 2006): 270–77.

Iwatsuki, Kunio, David E. Boufford, Hideaki Ohba, and Takashi Yamazaki, eds. *Flora of Japan.* 4 vols, 8 issues. Tokyo: Kodansha, 1993–2020.

La Scola, Bernard, Stéphane Audic, Catherine Robert, Liang Jungang, Xavier de Lamballerie, Michel Drancourt, Richard Birtles, Jean-Michel Claverie, and Didier Raoult. "A Giant Virus in Amoebae." *Science* (March 2003) 299: 2033.

Linnaeus, Carl. *Species Plantarum*. Stockholm: Laurentius Salvius, 1753.

Linnaeus, Carl. *Systema Naturae*. Leiden: 1753. 13th and final edition published in parts between 1788 and 1793; 10th edition, published in 1758 (Vol. 1) and 1759 (Vol. 2), accepted along with the first, 1753, edition of *Species Plantarum* as the starting points of zoological nomenclature.

Lovelock, James. The Ages of Gaia. Oxford: Oxford University Press, 1995.

Mayr, Ernst. *Principles of Systematic Zoology*. New York: McGraw-Hill Book Co., 1969.

Mayr, Ernst. *Systematics and the Origin of Species*. New York: Columbia University Press, 1942.

Myers, Norman, Russell Alan Mittermeier, Cristina G. Mittermeier, Gustavo Alberto Bouchardet da Fonseca, and Jennifer Kent. "Biodiversity Hotspots for Conservation Priorities." *Nature* 403 (February 2000): 853–58.

Mendel, Gregor. "Versuche über Pflanzen-hybriden" [Experiments on plant hybrids]. *Verhandlungen des naturforschenden Vereines in Brünn, Bd. IV für das Jahr 1865* (1866): 3–47.

Miller, Stanley L. "A Production of Amino Acids Under Possible Primitive Earth Conditions." *Science* 117 (May 1953): 528–29.

Nagata, Toshiyuki, and Itaru Tatebe. "Cell Wall Regeneration and Cell Division in Isolated Tobacco Mesophyll Protoplasts." *Planta* 92 (December 1970): 301–08.

Nagata, Toshiyuki, and Itaru Tatebe. "Plating of Isolated Tobacco Mesophyll Protoplasts on Agar Medium." *Planta* 99 (March 1971): 12–20.

Ray, John. *Historia Plantarum*. Vol. 1. London: Mariae Clark, 1686.

Reinert, Jonathan. "Morphogenese und ihre Kontrolle an Gewebekulturen aus Karotten" [Control of morphogenesis in cell cultures of carrots]. *Naturwissenschaft* 45 (1958): 344–45.

Steward, Frederick Campion, Marion O. Mapes, and Katheryn Mears. "Growth and Organized Development of Cultured Cells. II. Organization in Cultures Grown from Freely Suspended Cells." *American Journal of Botany* 45 (December 1958): 705–08.